When Lightning Strikes

Gilbert Vaux

Gilbert Vaux belongs to an old Somerset farming family, and before his massive stroke in 1986 ran a busy and successful farm with his wife and son. Despite working long hours he enjoyed public speaking, was a presenter for HTV West's *Country Farming* and sang with his local choral society.

The stroke left him severely disabled and temporarily without speech. Determination and sheer grit enabled him to once more speak in public, sing and act.

He is involved in the charity ADA (Aid for Dysphasic Adults), and The Phoenix Club in Yeovil and lives in South Petherton, Somerset.

GW00569393

WHEN LIGHTNING STRIKES

Life After a Stroke

Gilbert Vaux

Temple House Books
Sussex, England

Temple House Books
25 High Street,
Lewes, Sussex

First published 1994
© Gilbert Vaux 1994

Set in Times

Typesetting by PPS Limited, Amesbury, Wiltshire

Printed in Great Britain by
Athenæum Press Ltd.
Newcastle upon Tyne

A catalogue record for this book is
available from the British Library

ISBN 0 86332 943 8

CONTENTS

DEDICATION

This work is dedicated to the thousands of people who suffer a stroke every year, more especially my friends at the Phoenix Club, The Friends Meeting House, Goldcroft, Yeovil, whose cheerfulness and camaraderie have spurred me on. Although cast down by their disability, they will rise, phoenix-like, from the ashes of life.

FOREWORD
by Dr. N. W. Glendinning MD DRCOG

That Gilbert Vaux should write about his experiences and feelings following his stroke is not only of considerable interest for what he says, but a significant achievement in itself.

His vivid description of his sudden change from an active busy man, involved in his farm, family and the local community, into someone totally dependent on others, is both telling and dramatic.

My General Practice colleagues and I have watched with mounting admiration his fight back from severe disability with total dependence to his present independent state.

As he has described in this book, the support of his family and many friends, and in particular that of Peggy his wife, was vital.

However, he would have achieved nothing without his own remarkable determination.

He has been a lesson to all of us on what can be achieved if you have the courage and tenacity to keep going. For this reason, I am so pleased that he has written this book as it will encourage others. In it he shows, that however hard, long and hopeless the road back to independence may seem following a stroke, the struggle is always worthwhile. None of his doctors believed for a moment that he would attain anything like his present degree of independence. His book explains how this has been achieved and is achievable by others. Just as important, it highlights the need for prolonged support and encouragement from family and friends.

Anybody interested in post stroke rehabilitation, patients, friends and professional helpers alike, will find this 'view from within' a fascinating and informative book to read.

ACKNOWLEDGEMENTS

Many people have given help and encouragement in preparing this book. The medical staff at Yeovil District Hospital and South Petherton Hospital and my own doctors have been extremely kind and supportive. The therapists, both occupational and physiotherapists at the various hospitals or privately have given much encouragement as part of that therapy. I would also like to thank all those at the Apollo Club, Sherborne, among them Mike and Iris, Vic and John, Rachel and Barbara, Brian and Sue.

Ann Young, Brenda Joynes and Louise Ricketts have given invaluable advice and help in preparing the manuscript. Hundreds of friends have been supportive, especially in the darkest days.

I thank Tom and Kim Holt and Peter Spencer for the great interest they have shown in the book. Their professional approach has helped me enormously.

To my family and especially my wife, Peggy, no words of mine are sufficient to say 'thank you – with your combined love I have survived and lived to fight another challenge'.

INTRODUCTION

A stroke, also called a cerebro-vascular accident or apoplexy usually causes a sudden loss of consciousness and paralysis on one side of the body. The damage to the brain is a result of a blockage of an artery or bleeding from a ruptured artery in the brain. The paralysis occurs because of the damage to the part of the brain that controls the body movements. Conditions that are mainly responsible for strokes are *arterio-sclerosis* or hardening of the arteries; *hypertension* or high blood pressure and valvular disease of the heart.

A streak of lightning hits a tall oak tree and nearly destroys it. The tree is split from its topmost leaves and twigs, through its strongest branches to its roots.

That's how I felt when I had my stroke. Torn asunder. The very fabric of my being seemed to be rent in two.

From the top of my head to the toes of my right foot, as suddenly as I have written these few sentences and with no prior warning, my body was rendered useless.

Down from the top of my cranium through the right side of my face, my right cheek, the right side of my mouth, my lips, the spasticity was very intense. I became speechless in a minute or two. My right shoulder and my right arm had no feeling at all. The right side of my trunk became stiff almost at once. The right side of my pelvis was so stiff I couldn't work my right knee or my right ankle. Within two minutes I was completely immobile, speechless and very very frightened.

The records of our local hospital provide a good reference point and introduction.

Date patient admitted	July 13th, 1986
Time patient admitted	11.15 p.m.
Name of patient	Gilbert Newton Vaux
Address of patient	Rydon Farm, Compton Durville South Petherton, Somerset
Sex	Male
Age	58
Preliminary investigation	Massive cardio-vascular accident – condition was serious but not critical.

1

THE STROKE

As we get to middle age, we tend to think that life is fairly easy. Busy maybe, but kind nonetheless. I was a farmer. I thought I would go on farming until I was 65, have an active retirement, engage in some public work and probably write a book about 'Somerset Life'. Little did I think that those dreams could be shattered in 30 seconds, not from an accident but from a stroke.

The following story is not a fictional fragment from a fertile mind but a real-life story of one man's fall from a pinnacle and his fight to survive and live as a reasonably normal human being.

I say 'I was a farmer'. Not the 'chewing a piece of straw and leaning over a wooden gate, soaking up cider and watching the world go by' type farmer. I had received a good education – more of that later – and with my wife, Peggy, and our younger son Philip – our elder son Stephen had attained a Horticultural Degree and left practical farming to work abroad in developing countries – we had built up a successful vegetable plant-raising business. It had been my 'baby' for ten years and in 1986 we sold 17 million plants of various types. I say 'we' because right in the middle of the plant selling season, disaster struck and Peggy and my family, to their undying credit, did the work of keeping the customers – 450 of them – happy and the ship afloat.

1

I had this ghastly experience of the stroke in July 1986 and several months afterwards a doctor said, when asked what might have caused it, it could have been caused by one of three things. A higher than normal blood pressure, persistent smoking of cigars and stress. On thinking about my lifestyle over many years, I realised that the cigar smoking and the blood pressure had been merely contributory causes but the main problem had been the stress. Why had I undergone so much stress during the first 58 years of my life? I have tried to examine what has gone on throughout my life and in doing so I think I can trace a story which may be of interest to you as a reader.

To start with, my name has always created some interest. Strangers struggle to pronounce it wondering should it be 'Vaux' as in 'faux pas', or 'Vaux' as in 'Guy Fawkes'. They say, 'You must be of French descent, probably Huguenot'. 'Vaux' is actually a Norman name. At the time of the Norman Conquest of England in 1066, there was a nobleman in Normandy called 'Vaux'. He had three sons, Robert, Hubert and Gilbert.

They took family Mass at the small church of Dives sur Mer on the Normandy coast the night they sailed to England and the Battle of Hastings. Records show that Hubert and Robert founded religious communities in Norfolk and Cumberland. No trace can be found of Gilbert's family until the early 13th century when the record shows an Alice De Vaux of Seavington, a small community two miles west of my home village of South Petherton in Somerset. This has been faithfully recorded by Dr R. W. Dunning, official country historian who wrote the *Victorian History of Somerset*, volume 4. So we can safely say that the family has lived in this area of Somerset for over 700 years.

I mention this at the very beginning as this sense of

belonging to the farming fraternity, this longevity of ancestry, gave me something to hold on to during the darkest hours of the summer of 1986. My family have always been connected to the land, yeoman farmers or in modern terms, owner occupiers of land. From this very deep well of ancestry I have inherited an in-built understanding and feeling for the community in Somerset.

*

Some people like work. They seem to thrive on it. As an outdoor man living in the lovely Somerset countryside, it was just the very essence of my being. Eighty or a hundred hours a week spent with my business as a vegetable grower and merchant were common place. Until disaster struck. The type of disaster that is instantaneous and complete. I had a massive stroke as I was getting into bed on a Sunday night.

Sunday 13th July 1986 was a very busy day for me. It was very warm by 6 o'clock in the morning and I started work soon after that. My first customers started arriving to have their various leek plants before 7 o'clock. One hundred and twenty thousand were despatched from my rented refrigerated store, two miles from home, before 8.15. I then inspected my twenty-five acre field of various vegetable plants before a quick conference with my pig man.

'How many pigs will be going this week, Clive?'
'I don't know, we shall be weighing them tomorrow.'
'Do you want any more skim milk this week?'
'Yes, I'll have a load on Tuesday afternoon.'
'Would you want any meal or any nuts this week, for the pigs?'
'No, I shan't want any nuts but I shall want a load of meal on Friday.'

'Right, that's fine.'

'Terry and I will be available to help you with the plants tomorrow morning at about half past eleven.'

I then had my breakfast and spent the rest of the morning in my office. There were a million leek plants to be despatched within two or three days. How many plants had to go to whom? Would they be required to go by rail from Taunton Station or be collected from the farm? They all had to be cleared before the end of the week as there were another million plants expected from Holland on the following Saturday. As if this wasn't a big enough job there were Brussels sprouts, cauliflower, cabbage, calabrese, savoy cabbage, January King and other varieties of plants to be pulled and sold – up to 300 thousand per day. A Herculean task, I now freely admit.

My father-in-law came for Sunday lunch and I recharged some flagging batteries with a snooze until 3.00 p.m. Under the blazing afternoon sun, I trimmed the hedge in front of the house and by half past seven, father-in-law was ready to be taken home by Peggy. This left me with the last job to be done for the day.

The vegetable plants were pulled one at a time. They were bundled with elastic bands into 50s and sold in 1,000's in new strong five-ply paper bags. Each bag had a panel on it showing to whom they were consigned, their destination, the total number of bags, and the person that pulled them. All these bags had to be marked before I could go to bed.

I must tell you that all the time throughout the day (as had been the case over the last ten years) I had been smoking, probably more than ten cigars per day. This no doubt contributed to what followed. Eventually all the various jobs were finished for the day and I had a cup of tea and was ready for bed.

4

I had a shower and tried to revive my aching limbs. I got into bed about quarter to eleven and Peggy got in beside me. No sooner had she got into bed, than she realised that the alarm clock had not been altered for the morning. She got out and changed it. I said 'I think there is something wrong with my leg'.

She came and had a look at me and we agreed that the doctor should be called. I had no feeling in my right leg, or in my right arm, or down the whole of the right side of my body. It is hardly possible to realise that what had been an active man could be reduced to an immobile hulk in probably less than 30 seconds.

The doctor arrived within a few minutes and although I was not told, he obviously realised that I had suffered from a stroke. The ambulance was called from Yeovil Hospital and arrived within half an hour. During that time many thoughts passed through my mind.

Surely this won't last very long?

I should be better tomorrow morning.

I should be able to get up and be able to do my normal day's work.

My staff will be expecting me to be on duty as normal at 7.00 a.m.

My customers will expect me to be on duty from 7.15 in the morning

There was no thought going through my mind of being completely incapable of doing any physical work.

I can remember the doctor carrying out various tests on my right leg and my left leg, my right elbow and my left elbow. He carried out very basic tests upon my eyesight. Two fingers were put up in front of my eyes and my reaction to them was observed as they moved in front of my face. My vision was already affected.

Whilst the ambulance was coming to fetch me, I drifted off into some form of sleep. Peggy and the doctor moved my right arm onto the bed because it had been hanging lifeless beside the bed until then.

The ambulance attendants arrived and were absolutely superb. I was put onto the stretcher and carried downstairs and into the waiting ambulance. Then came the journey to Yeovil Hospital.

A matter of about nine miles and it took twenty minutes. During that time I became very nauseated and eventually was sick. But I still did not lose consciousness.

When we arrived at the hospital and I was moved into the casualty ward, doctors and nurses gathered round very quickly and I began to get confused as to what was happening at that time. I may have been given a sedative or it may have been the effects of the stroke. After that, I lost consciousness and was tucked up into some bed or other but I really don't know how I got there. I was in the intensive care unit throughout the next twenty-four hours.

It is important now to remember certain very basic facts about those first hours. When the stroke struck, I moved from a position of being a fit man of 58 to a wreck. The length of time taken to reach that situation was no more than 30 seconds.

Those first agonizing hours when I returned to a state of semi-normal consciousness were most distressing. I tried to open my eyes and they seemed to be completely filled with a mucus. I couldn't see properly. Alarm bells rang. Perhaps I should be blind or partially sighted as my grandmother had been throughout her life. I had to try and wipe away the muck from my face. I couldn't use my right hand and my left hand had to swing across my face. It was altogether most distressing. I couldn't control my eyes anyway. The muscles at the back of the right eye had been badly affected. I could just about see images from my left eye but nothing from my right.

Because the right eye couldn't see anything I had to open the left eye much wider than normal so that I appeared to be staring. This abnormality continued for at least a year.

I have looked back now after eight years to try and analyse why it happened. Maybe I was smoking too much. Fifteen to twenty cigars a day would appear to be far too many. Maybe I was working too hard and in this book I shall recount the sort of life that I was leading. It had been a life filled with stress of one sort and another. That stress had to find a way out of my system.

I did have a certain amount of high blood pressure but had rather ignored any warnings which I had had. On reflection and with my father and mother's history of blood pressure and inter-related problems, this may have been a major contributory cause.

Anyway, what happened on Sunday July 13th, 1986 at approximately 11.00 p.m. is now history. But life has to go on and I have had to continue fighting from that day onwards until now. I shall do so for the rest of my life to show other people that all is not lost when one is faced with such a traumatic experience.

In writing this book, I will try and explain exactly what it was like during my hospitalisation. How many people helped me to reach some form of normality and how my Cancerian spirit has never failed me.

It has been a bitter struggle but it is a struggle that may have a silver lining. Perhaps it has been a stroke of luck that I can at least speak, comprehend, write and I trust give hope to others who may be struck down in this way.

2

THE FIRST FEW DAYS

When I arrived at Yeovil Hospital, no mention was made of 'a stroke'. Why should it be? This was only going to be a temporary inconvenience. The hospital would get me back on my feet in time to start work on Monday morning.

I felt I was too busy to be ill – I couldn't afford to be ill. I couldn't think straight.

There were those thousands of leek plants to get on the various trains during the week. There would be many customers coming to collect their plants on Monday afternoon after 6.00 p.m.

Peggy had come to the hospital in our car and had alerted our two sons, Stephen and Philip together with their wives, Jenny and Sandra, and informed them at that stage what was happening. She was told by the doctors that it was a grave situation but that, as I was already in hospital, every effort would be made to save my life.

Confusion was setting in at this time.

Hell was it really like this?

Fear – fright – would those customers get their plants?

Death – was it really so awful?

Confusion – injection – hallucination – nightmares – sleep – sleep – sleep.

Monday July 14th

I awoke but at what time I don't know. I couldn't move. My right leg wouldn't move. My right arm – my right hand. They hung motionless by my side.

I was aware that doctors and nurses were working around me. I couldn't really see them. All images seemed to be very confused. The stroke had affected the vision in my right eye. The muscles at the back of the right eye were not in tune with the muscles of the left eye. In consequence I couldn't see with my right eye at all.

At some time during the day I was helped out of bed. Two nurses supported me as I tried to move along the side of it.

There was agonizing pain throughout the right side of my body. It was filled with tingling as though the nerve endings were all exposed. The nurses tried to walk me around the bed. By the time we had reached the bottom of the bed, perhaps six feet, I was unable to go any further. Sweat was pouring from my brow.

The nurses got me back into bed and any further exercise had to be abandoned. The pain was most distressing and I cried bitterly.

Peggy visited me that day with my elder son, Stephen. His kiss when he left my bedside reassured my confused brain that I was supported by my family. I knew I was very ill. Many expressions from many people came with that kiss.

Tuesday July 15th

I had survived another night. But real fear was beginning to settle within my mind. How could my wife, my family, my staff manage to keep my complex business on an even

9

keel and in full working order? (They did and I am eternally grateful to them.)

Some form of therapy started in the morning. A male orderly took me in a wheelchair down in the lift to the physiotherapy department of the hospital. The therapist carried out some very basic tests.

Could my eyes focus on the two fingers in front of my face?

Could they move from side to side and follow the fingers?

Was there any reflex action when my right elbow or my right knee was struck with a reflex hammer?

Was there any reaction when the bottom of my right foot was tickled?

I was very confused and can only just remember what was happening to me at that time.

Whilst I was in the physiotherapy department an old acquaintance saw me. I had known her for more than forty years. She was very shocked to see me there as she had not been told of my sudden illness. She spoke to me and asked how I was. I recognised her voice but was unable to make any speech at all. However I did manage to wink! She tells me she thought I should survive having seen me do that!

I seemed extremely tired throughout this period. Rest and some sleep, even with the aid of tablets, was all that I seemed to be capable of doing. The nurses tried to get me out of bed on all occasions to keep my body movements going. Thrombosis had to be avoided if possible.

Visitors came to see me every afternoon and evening. My family and my closest friends were my constant companions during visiting hours. Many of them were very shocked to see me.

Some friends from Taunton have told me since that

having seen me they both – man and wife – travelled home, a matter of twenty-five miles and said nothing to one another throughout the journey.

That night I had the most awful nightmare. I felt I was one of that helpless band of Jewish men and women moving slowly across the barren waste that surrounded the Belsen Concentration Camp. The gas chambers loomed up in front of me. There was no turning back. My turn was coming. I was about to move inside the building. Suddenly the German officer in command was confronted by some young beautiful girl. The order was barked out 'stop the day's work'.

I had been reprieved at the last moment. I awoke bathed in sweat, frightened, trembling, tears flowing with uncontrolled grief.

The following afternoon I remember another incident vividly. My father-in-law came to see me. He was about 86 at the time. He was most distressed to see my condition. He looked at me and his eyes told me exactly how he was feeling. He felt he would never see me again. However, he did not realise that I was born under the Cancerian sign. Although I am not a great believer in astrology, I feel many times that my crab-like nature which enables me to hold on to any problem until it is solved, stood me in good stead. Crabs never let go. I resolved from that moment that I would survive, that I would talk again and be as normal as I possibly could be. I had always been very keen on ballroom dancing with Peggy. The desire to return to normality was combined with my desire to get back to ballroom dancing. As time has gone by my sense of rhythm has somewhat departed but it would be nice if I could dance again.

As well as these incidents of depression, I suffered the indignity of incontinence one night. Fortunately it has only occurred on one occasion. However I felt mentally

11

drained of all emotion and could be only thankful for the wonderful care of the nursing staff.

Four days after going into hospital there was one important job which I had to get done. All cheques on my business account had required just my signature at the time of being presented at the bank. Peggy and Philip were my partners but not signatories to our cheques. The bank required a mandate for this to be changed. Peggy brought in the necessary forms and it was a super-human effort to sign those papers. But by signing them Philip and Peggy were able to carry on the business. Peggy worked very closely with the bank and Jenny, my daughter-in-law was a great help in preparing accounts over the next eight weeks. This, at least, was a relief.

At a very early stage, maybe within the first two or three days, I carried out an examination of my lips and mouth, cheeks and jaws to find out what was wrong with me. I found that the right side of my face, lips and nose and the inside of my mouth as far as the centre, were numb. The muscles of my mouth were not seriously affected and dribbling of food, which can be such a distressing thing for those who are badly affected with stroke, thankfully never occurred.

I was able to recognise words and understand what people were saying to me but I couldn't make any sensible reply. Communication through speech has always been an important part of life to me. I have never used painting or sculpture to convey my feelings. I felt that the power of conversation – the spoken word, has always been the greatest attribute than any person could have. To lose it completely is to lose direct contact with humanity.

In my case, I never lost the power of comprehension. There were many things done for me and to me, but, I was never completely unaware of what was happening.

Saying what was in my mind, how I felt, what I wanted,

was extremely difficult. The frustration and the confusion were intense. Rarely a man to lose my temper, I felt the anger build up into a rage until tears were my only outlet. To these pangs of anger must be added the worry I felt for my business.

Five million leek plants were needed from Holland. When would they arrive? Would they all be distributed? Would they all be paid for within a week (our normal terms of trading were cash in seven days). Would there be enough Savoy cabbage or cauliflower plants to satisfy the customers' requirements? How were the potatoes yielding? Dozens and dozens of thoughts flashed through my mind, but my body was powerless to do anything about them.

I had to be fed first from a feeding beaker and then the nurses helped me eat normally. It was always a problem as at that time I was unable to find my mouth into which to put my own food. My lips and cheeks could not function normally, I couldn't hold my head up in the normal way. It hung down on my right shoulder. Meal times were a constant effort and had to be followed by a period of rest before the next visitors arrived.

On day ten, I well remember the celebrations in the ward as patients were wheeled in their beds to witness on television the marriage of Prince Andrew and Miss Sarah Ferguson. Normally I should have enjoyed such an occasion, but, half an hour of watching completely exhausted me and by the time I had drawn the attention of a nurse to my problems, I was somewhat distressed.

Excitement of any kind seemed to be the one emotion that I could not take. Even today I cannot cope with sustained periods of anger.

My friends were absolutely marvellous as they supported me and gave my whole family help in so many ways. Unfortunately there were some who could not conceal their true feelings of fear that I would not survive, or at best be a chair-bound cripple.

May I say to all who visit the sick, 'never go visiting unless you are prepared to leave your emotions at the ward entrance. It is hard enough to fight back depression. A stroke patient does not want the added distress of a normal person, however sincere and well meaning they may be. Grief and tears must be kept outside the hospital.'

Peggy, Stephen and Philip had many tasks to tackle. Peggy had several bookings for our farmhouse bed and breakfast accommodation. Stephen was occupied, at that time, with his work as a co-ordinator for the local farmers' potato co-operative. Philip had his contract potato lifting to be organised. Wages had to be met. Staff had to be supervised. The telephone, which rarely stopped ringing, had to be answered.

My mind very soon returned to some state of normality but the body was useless. It was hell at the time but to my family's unfailing credit they were not found wanting. While I would not like to go through those difficult days again, I did survive. Surviving with a stroke of luck, to recall and retell the inside story of a cerebral-vascular accident.

3

HARD WORK BEGINS

On day eleven, the doctors said I was fit to move to South Petherton Hospital. This unit was originally an Isolation Hospital built in the 1930's. At that time, tuberculosis, scarlet fever and other similar diseases were quite common in the district. Now the hospital has been updated to full modern standards and acts as a convalescent home for patients from Yeovil General Hospital. It has forty-four beds and eight separate cubicles for private patients or those who may be very ill. The resident Matron is supported by four full time Sisters and a full complement of nurses and orderlies. There is a small Radiography Department and Physiotherapy and Occupational Therapy Departments.

Saturday July 26th

I was helped to dress thinking all the time 'going home to South Petherton at last'. I was taken by wheelchair to the waiting ambulance. The journey took twenty-five minutes – minutes of sadness, exhaustion, hope, frustration. I had left Yeovil General Hospital for the last time as a bedridden patient. On arrival I was welcomed by faces I had known all my life. I was undressed and returned to bed. I was in a General Ward containing eight beds. One or two of the patients were terminally ill. Some were young men recovering from motoring accidents. Some were old men who had had abdominal operations. The ward was kept immaculately clean and the food was first class. The first two days were spent getting acclimatised and settled in.

I could not speak normally at this stage. I could make myself understood by the nurses. I was in pain – not the sort of pain associated with a cut finger or strained back but pain nevertheless. The following passage contains details supplied by the Physiotherapy Department at South Petherton Hospital setting out what was done to me and for me in the succeeding weeks when I was an in-patient at the hospital.

South Petherton Hospital – 28th July 1986

Passive movement, stretches and sitting balance

The therapist very gently moved my right arm away from my body a distance of six inches. This was repeated six times.

My right arm was stretched from its curled up position. It was very painful and three times was enough.

I was seated on the side of the bed and encouraged to sit upright. Without support, I toppled over as I had no sense of balance.

29th July 1986

Similar to 28.7.86. Progressed to bridging and rolling exercises.

16

I was made to bridge my back as many times as possible when lying down in bed to loosen the spasticity in my pelvis.

The rolling exercises had a similar effect.

31st July 1986

Much more orientated, standing in a frame with back supported. Weight transference over right leg.

I had begun to realise what was happening to me.

Nurses helped the physiotherapist to put me in a frame. One stayed behind me to give my back support.

I was required to put some weight on my right foot. This was very difficult. I did not realise I had a right foot. The spasticity or stiffness in my right leg and right foot was very intense. Again there was pain, but pain is a natural trial we all have to bear so bear it I must.

5th August 1986

Stood for ten minutes with a lot of assistance. Encouragement of extension of right knee – no active hip flexion in standing. Sitting balance exercises and bilateral arm exercises.

I was undoubtedly able to stand for a reasonable length of time but I needed considerable help to do so. There was encouragement to extend my right knee but there was no movement in the hip whatsoever. I was getting better at balancing when sitting on a padded bench.

17

8th August 1986

> Passive movements to the right arm as there was no active
> movement. Some movement in the right leg – hip and knee
> flexion, some quadriceps and a slight flicker of movement
> in the right ankle. Work in the physiotherapy department
> in the afternoon in rolling and balancing. Stood between
> parallel bars with the help of two people. Balance in sitting
> good but poor in standing.

There was undoubtedly some encouragement in the
various movements that were taking place at that time.
I was making some progress.

10th August 1986

> Walked between two people – some control of right knee
> but not all the time. Tires very easily still.

I was making some progress in walking with some control
of my right leg.

Those long days of regular physiotherapy which
enlivened the hours of rest and recuperation were
interrupted with incidents of melancholy and mirth, strain
and stress.

One night was most distressing for me when I trapped
my unfeeling arm under my body. It was the action of
an unconscious brain. I had fallen asleep on my back
and had rolled on my right side without the normal
practice of withdrawing my arm to a position where
circulation of the blood would flow normally.

I awoke sometime during the night to indescribable
pain. My right arm was under my body and for several
hours I knew the meaning of hell on earth.

Nurses came to release my arm but I cried out in pain.

I awoke the rest of the ward with my screaming and one elderly patient, who was becoming very senile, came over to my bed and asked me to shut up.

I replied in suitable English with the few well-chosen words 'bugger off and mind your own business!!'

Thank God that occasion has not happened again and I guard against it for fear of being subjected to similar flames of suffering.

A tall, blonde, night nurse came and soothed my brow. A massive dose of painkilling tablets had to be given. They gave some relief. During those two or three hours of indescribable pain, I sank to the very bottom of my resistance. I felt completely exhausted, without hope. I was at the very nadir of my life. I felt I would soon be facing my Maker. I had to unburden myself – lose all those feelings of inadequacy, the self doubts and fears of my earlier life, all those feelings of guilt – all had to be washed away in the floods of tears that night.

I could breathe. I could blink. I dared not move a muscle. I cried but it was the nurse who had to wipe away my tears. My pyjamas had to be changed twice at least during the night as I was sweating in pain. I lay motionless, not daring to move. Eventually, sleep overtook me about 4.30 in the morning. I was drained of all emotion and had no resistance left.

Next morning, I awoke shattered and dispirited and the routine of the day had to be curtailed. The normal washing procedure together with teeth cleaning were shortened to an assisted wash down of the face before I settled back to recharge the run down batteries of my very run down body.

The physiotherapist dispensed with any therapy that day. The distress of this incident was sharpened into even greater emphasis later that day. There are dismal Jimmys in every circle of acquaintances. My circle contains a few people who come in this category. One person came to see me and we chatted about the usual things – the weather, the family, the Government, and the farming trade in general. Then I heard a long story about how bad things were for him and what could he do to get out of his difficulties. There seemed to be an unending catalogue of catastrophes. The conversation was downhill and one way only.

Eventually I had to ask him to leave. How thankful I was that my true friends were not like that or I should never have recovered.

Probably the person was not aware that his remarks were distressing. But may I put in a plea here to all who may visit the sick. Please be careful to avoid such an occurrence – it is selfish, unnecessary, unkind. That 'I' of the visitor is not what the patient wants to hear, the 'You' is more important.

I must mention a further incident on hospital visiting time. Everyone has friends who are sympathetic and well meaning and enjoy the sort of jokes that make us all laugh. Unfortunately this merriment was carried too far when certain business colleagues came round one afternoon. After kind enquiries about my health and how the business was going, they burst into the inevitable jokes gleaned from golf courses, rugby dinners, business lunches or from other business acquaintances. The first few stories were most amusing but after half an hour of hearing one man's voice it was too much.

Please try to emulate the kind of approach which is used by one gentleman and his wife who must be accorded a bouquet for the way in which they do their visiting: they always arrive early, they are never late, they are always cheerful (even if they feel terrible themselves) and never stay more than a quarter of an hour.

I hasten to add that these comments do not apply to those who may be visiting their immediate family or those who have travelled a considerable distance to attend their friends.

The great event in that first week at South Petherton Hospital was to be a bath. Not a strip wash by the bedside but a proper bath with soapsuds and full body immersion. It sounded wonderful. But, how could I get into a bath, and even more important, how could I get out of the bath?

A male nurse sat me in a normal wheelchair which was supported by a hoist arrangement hanging over the side of the bath. Ecstasy and relief!! I felt I could live again and gentle hands helped me to lather myself and refresh my tired limbs.

What was wrong with my right leg and my right arm?

Why didn't my right leg and arm help with the washing process or respond to my mental demands by bending my right leg?

It may sound stupid and elementary now, but rest assured, at that time these were very real feelings.

I had at this time begun speaking again. I had been very proud of my Somerset accent. Now though, it was very rough with a distinct burr to the 'r's. I was hesitant about speaking sentences containing more than four words. 'How are you?' 'I am well'. 'Nice day, sunny isn't it?' – I could manage these phrases quite normally at that time.

Getting my tongue around some words, such as 'characteristically' was very difficult, so I used different words. The 'natural communicator' would not be beaten. My speech was rather slower and more deliberate than normal but I taught myself how to control my tongue and my lips. 'Practice does make perfect' is the old saying and I have practised loud and long. Today I am near perfect, I think.

The swelling inside my mouth extended from my right cheek to the middle of my left. The lower right jaw seemed divorced from other areas of my mouth. I have never received any speech therapy. Perhaps the professional speech therapist realised I was having therapy from the many friends who were visiting me.

Sport, politics, foreign news were always topics of conversations. What was happening on my farm? What were the prospects for the corn harvest?

Stroke patients may have difficulty with their speech, but must not be ignored or side tracked just because the normal processes of communication have been impaired. A BBC radio programme for the visually handicapped is called *Does He Take Sugar*. The title is taken from the habit of some people not to speak to a handicapped person but to ask their companion. Ask the *stroke patient himself* a simple question. The patient does understand the question. He (or she) just requires more time than usual to give an answer.

Time was the one thing that was needed. Time to react when having any conversation with staff or visitors. Time to allow the brain to send messages from the eyes or ears to the mouth, voice box and lips.

I have always greatly prized the ability to articulate well. Some may have said in the past before I had my stroke, that I talked too much. Always on some soapbox, some people said. A shy person who suffers from a stroke could quickly become cut off from normal conversation. Verbal communication is a heaven-sent blessing, never to be undervalued.

The physiotherapy continued twice daily on a Monday to Friday basis. The treatment seemed very basic as I merely had to extend my spastic hand and arm over a large ball and rock it forwards and backwards for as long as I was able to do so. Little did I realise how important this exercise was.

The stroke had removed the elasticity from the limbs. The sensation that one feels when a pin pricks ones toes never left me. But the movement of my right toes and my right ankle, my right knee and right shoulder and most particularly my right hand and right arm had been severely restricted.

It would appear to a layman and a stroke sufferer that the human body consists of bones which are supported on all sides by nerves rather like a stocking supported by a garter. The brain makes the legs function by sending messages via those nerves to flex the muscles which are attached to every bone and cause the limb to alter its position. The brain sends messages and the leg moves forwards and backwards.

For the stroke sufferer, this complicated process is interrupted. When the clot of blood burst within my head, some of the millions of cells that were within the brain were damaged or destroyed. For the unfortunate few, damage to the brain is complete and death soon follows.

Elastic garters, which we have all worn at our schools to keep our socks up, provide a good illustration of what I felt at the time. A garter can be stretched and stretched. It eventually snaps. The right leg, the right side of the pelvis, the right arm and the right hand felt just like that. Added to this spasticity in these limbs was confusion in the brain and difficulties with articulating words.

Therapy had to reawaken some parts of the brain so that limbs could begin to function normally. To start with, I had to learn to turn over in bed without trapping my right arm. The right arm felt nothing, so the brain said nothing to the right arm. Likewise, the right leg did not respond to any messages and my right foot and my right leg lay motionless in the bed.

15th August 1986

Great improvement – better control of the right knee. Still no movement in the right arm. Balance in prone kneeling and kneeling good. Exercises on the mat and on the floor.

I was undoubtedly making some improvement at that time with some better control of my right leg and right knee. I was beginning to feel that I could balance in a more normal position.

18th August 1986

Tried walking with a tripod and two people to encourage weight transference. Further mat work. Still no movement in right arm.

19th August 1986

Walking forwards, backwards and sideways in the parallel bars in the physiotherapy room. Finds sideways difficult as hip abductors weak. Further mat work. Not aware of position of toes and ankle when eyes are shut. Still only a flicker of movement in the right ankle. Aware of position of right shoulder and right elbow but not right wrist or fingers with eyes shut.

I was having some confusion when my eyes were kept shut.

22nd August 1986

Improved – needed less assistance in walking with a tripod.

24

25th August 1986

> When able to concentrate one hundred per cent and not be too tired, is almost independently walking with a stick. Needs only help of one person. Can move from sitting to standing position without help. Standing and balance improving.

26th August 1986

> Fantastic improvement – Virtually independent with an ordinary walking stick. Still no movement in the right arm.

I was obviously pleasing the physiotherapist very much at that time and had changed from using a tripod to an ordinary walking stick.

30th August 1986

> Slight spasticity in the right arm. Some pain with passive movements to shoulder. Maintaining full passive range of movements in the right shoulder. Can stand well unaided. Walking on the ward a lot – only needs help occasionally when balance goes. Started static bicycle work.

This involved using a normal static exercise bicycle. When seated on the bicycle, the physiotherapist supported me as I had no sense of balance, the whole of the right side of my body seemed to possess no strength. At first I just toppled over to one side. After a few minutes I seemed to have more normal control. My left foot and left leg did a little pedalling, the right foot and leg being dragged along whilst the brain tried making my limbs go in a circular movement.

As can be seen from these notes, the physiotherapist was not making an entry every day although I was being treated twice daily on a Monday to Friday basis.

I am often asked: did I despair? Did I lose heart or the will to win the battle in which I found myself? Of course there were moments of despair but I felt I must struggle on. So many people were willing me on. So many prayers had been said. So much help had beeen given to Peggy and my family that I couldn't let them down.

Above all, I am a cussed bugger. I had been a physically strong man of fifty-eight despite being a heavy cigar smoker for ten years. I felt inwardly that I would survive – I would walk and talk again.

8th September 1986

> Went home for the day – four days in all over the Bank Holiday period. Came back to the hospital to sleep at night. Seemed to manage OK. But admits to one fall. Right shoulder very painful when on full passive range movements. Now has some spasticity in the right leg.

9th September 1986

> First movement noticed in right hand – flickers of flexion in thumb, index, middle and ring fingers. Walked half a circuit of hospital grounds with a stick. Only lost his balance once.

This incident of walking the hospital grounds underlines my inbuilt habit of clock watching. A lifelong employer, I had always striven to plough more acres in a day or expected more plants to be pulled today compared with

26

yesterday. I just had to walk further each day.

The first day I walked half a circuit of the hospital grounds in twenty minutes with a rest in the physiotherapy department. Next day I followed the same routine taking nineteen and a half minutes. Next day nineteen minutes.

I had to force my aching body through the pain barriers to reach the end of the very dark tunnel.

16th September 1986 (Tuesday)

> Home visit with me to see if he could cope with stairs with a view to going home for a weekend. Coped OK Home Saturday a.m., sleeping home Saturday night, back to hospital Sunday evening.

Although the physiotherapist's report says that I coped with stairs in a satisfactory manner, this was not strictly true.

Our large hamstone five-bedroomed house at Rydon Farm was in an elevated position. From the garden path to the front door is five steps. From the rear passageway to the back door are four large stone steps. The stairs to the first floor bedrooms are normal to most people – to me it seemed like climbing a mountain.

There were four steps with a small landing where one turned through ninety degrees. Twelve steps further up before turning again. There were four steps to the landing. Getting upstairs with assistance from Peggy and my physiotherapist was tiring work with beads of perspiration on my brow.

The bedroom which held such bittersweet memories beckoned. An extension to the house enabling us to have an en-suite bathroom was an absolute godsend.

27

Getting downstairs was quite another problem. There was no handrail on the left-hand side. I dreaded falling downstairs because though two people were there to save me, I knew a thirteen-stone man who feels he is dead weight takes some stopping when falling downstairs. Numerous attempts were made to walk down normally. Eventually and very reluctantly, I sat myself down and descended on my bottom. (Since then I have learned a much better way – walk down backwards!)

That first night at home was a very restless one with only a little sleep. I could not bear the second body in the bed. Was I really rejecting my wife of thirty-six years? I had been alone with my own body for fifty-five days. I felt ashamed of my own body, not wishing to be hugged and kissed.

The bedclothes bore down too heavily on my spastic right foot, especially the big toe. The right arm and right hand had to be helped at all times to a more comfortable position.

We immediately decided that twin beds were the answer. The uncomfortable *feeling of bed warmth would disappear completely* to be replaced with more contented, more normal sleep.

19th September 1986

> Home visit with physiotherapist and occupational therapist to discuss rails and adjustments at home.

The physiotherapist and the occupational therapist came to see what handrails could be provided on the NHS. Handrails might be needed at doors with steps. Handrails might be needed at upstairs and downstairs toilets. Every form of practical assistance from these members of staff was given. Due to the large number of quite deep steps into the premises and the variable elevations within the house, it was not an ideal place for a severely disabled person to move around. In retrospect, these difficulties may have been a kind of benefit. If I wanted to get back to some sort of normal existence, the hurdles which had to be negotiated had to be a little harder, more trying than I would have liked.

22nd September 1986

> Home to sleep overnight again. Can now walk whole circuit of hospital grounds with his stick and me at the side but giving no support.

From September 22nd to September 28th I was having a new brand of treatment – getting used to living outside the hospital routine. Perhaps I should be home in a week or two.

23rd September 1986

> Walking over difficult obstacles on the floor and up and down grassy slopes in hospital grounds. Managed very well.

24th September 1986

> Home for three nights. All OK.

27th September 1986

> Out to silver wedding party in evening and slept home at night.

This was my first adventure out into the normal world. Some farmer friends who live a few miles away wanted us to join them and fifty other guests at their party which was held at their home. We arrived at 8.15 p.m. and I was brought in in a wheelchair.

My eyesight had been affected. Getting people into focus was the problem. Fifty people milling around, mainly wanted to see me and wish me well. I have been told since that one lady whom I knew slightly, swept out of the room in floods of tears as she had not seen me in hospital. By half past nine the noise, and the movement had exhausted me and we went home and I was glad to get to bed.

26th September 1986

Home for weekend. If all successful will stay home for good.

29th September 1986

All OK, so is now to attend three times a week at the hospital as an outpatient.

Before talking about going home, I want to say a big thank you to the doctors, nurses – male and female, orderlies and the therapists for their professional attention, their cheerfulness, their kindnesses. I couldn't have got this far without you.

4

THE DIFFICULT DAYS

Those early days after I returned home were ones of confusion, frustration, anger and depression. Why couldn't I get up at 6.30 in the morning as I used to?

Why couldn't I get on my tractor and do some driving?

Why couldn't I answer the telephone?

Why couldn't I sign cheques for wages or pay money into the bank?

Why did I take an hour to dress and why was it necessary to have Peggy help me do so all the time?

Why couldn't I read the paper and why did I fall asleep every hour or so?

Why? Why? Why?

I cursed myself for getting in such a position and I cursed myself for not being able to get out of the totally restricted life which the stroke had inflicted upon me. I felt alone – oh, so lonely – for I could not attempt to do what I had done before. I had been a one hundred per cent man. I had led my business and any organisation from the front. I felt neglected. I felt without any prospect for real improvement.

I felt likely to remain dependent upon other people for my food and drink, my dressing and undressing, my shaving and washing. There was continued pain in my limbs. They felt all swollen. The pain and anguish were unbearable. I often cried, sometimes for ten minutes at a time.

I know now how much my family and my friends cared about me and I can only offer my sincere apologies if I appeared offhand. I was very worried about myself and I was in danger of becoming selfish and self-centred which was completely alien to me.

My peripheral vision was restricted and I seemed to lose the ability to turn my head to the right. My eyes didn't focus and the right side of my face had little or no feeling so I felt I need not bother to use it at any time.

Any fears of self-doubt or self-pity needed arresting quickly. I could not continue as a complete invalid, wallowing in my own misfortune and receiving full time care. I had to get up and get out on the road of life.

I had to get used to travelling much slower. I had to accept that my whole life had been changed. Gone out of my life was dancing. Gone out of my life was activity of any sort.

But I had to fight back. I was surrounded by my wife, my family and hundreds of friends, all of whom supported me. All willing me on to get better.

My earliest efforts upon this road to recovery were agonising, and tiring. The farm had a private drive which was 375 yards long from the farmhouse to the public highway. It was a tarmac drive and carried only my farm tractors and implements. It was a quiet road and not overlooked by anyone. This provided the ideal outlet for my frustrations and my efforts to overcome my nervousness and pain. It was an excellent goal, or more particularly a series of goals to attain.

At first I could only manage to walk ten yards down the drive. Then a pause for a little while. Then back again. This exercise may have taken ten minutes.

The next day I felt stronger. I felt I could walk fifteen yards.

And so it continued until I was able to walk the three hundred and seventy five yards. It wasn't until I had been walking for at least two months that I could manage to do the length of the whole drive.

I had to have another person, usually Peggy, beside me. Not to give me any physical assistance. I just needed reassurance.

I had always enjoyed walking in the rain. Now even the threat of a shower of rain filled me with fear. I loathed walking on slippery surfaces.

Many times I have stood still while Peggy fetched the car to take me home. Maybe I had walked only one hundred yards, but, I was scared of falling over on any wet roads.

At about that time Peggy had received some good advice from our doctors. She had read about the work done by friends of Patricia Neal, the actress, who had an even more severe stroke than myself many years ago. She had been very ill and her friends had taken it in turns to stir her from a very low state. After years of progress she was able to stand, to speak normally, to memorise her parts and to return to her former profession as an actress.

This was the spur that I needed and I resolved, there and then, that I would get back into a fairly normal state of action. Some people thought that it couldn't be done. Inbuilt within my character is a Cancerian instinct. I never let go.

I had a strong physical constitution. Without it, I should never have survived.

I had devoted attention from Peggy and my family. I had marvellous friends.

There were nevertheless a few Doubting Thomases. 'I doubt if he can do it'. 'He will always be confined to a wheelchair'. 'He will never be independent.'

It was said, I know, by a few. It was certainly thought

by many.

Attempting to walk was not enough. Playing the game of Scrabble had to take the place of mental stimulation which I greatly missed as my business contacts had been shattered. I played Scrabble on Tuesday and Thursday mornings with a series of lady friends. Their patience and humour, their good fellowship and love kept me sane and I owe them a great debt of gratitude. I could not make words of more than four letters and often had to finish our session before all the letters had been used up. Sometimes our games took over an hour and my score rarely exceeded 160. Now Peggy and I regularly exceed 300 each when playing and have occasionally reached 400.

Rest has always had to follow any effort. Rest, even without sleep, is such an important part of the recovery process. The human body punishes itself for so much of the time that it is a wonder that there aren't more accidents, more marriage breakdowns, more murders and rapes, more heart attacks and more strokes. Maybe life is too fast, too demanding, without lasting reward and for many, without hope of ever rising from the great slough of despondency which seems to grasp the stroke sufferer so often.

Visitors came from far and wide displaying great sympathy and encouragement to get well soon.

Many people were very nervous of meeting me again. Some only stayed a few minutes. Due to my hesitant jumbled speech, some found conversation very difficult, whilst others left with a lame excuse.

The vision of my right eye was severely impaired. I was not able to control the eyeball within the socket.

I looked very different to many people. Some I know found visiting me very stressful at first. There were even some who thought they might catch a stroke as one catches the measles. 'I mustn't get too close to him' I could feel them thinking. 'He has been very ill. Perhaps I may be the next'.

To all who came I can only say 'thank you' for your attention, your concern, your sympathy and your love. Without these things I should have drifted into the slough of mediocrity and been a poor citizen of life.

The normal joys of the Christmas season seemed to pass us by. So much of our normal visiting of friends, our singing for the local Combined Arts Society and our toasting of 'Good Health and Happiness' seemed to fall into insignificance as I tried to recover my composure.

I could not drink nor visit any friends. Normally I had sung Christmas carols with my many friends in our Combined Arts Society Choir. I could not face the crowd at our family celebration at Christmas. This normally takes place on the Sunday after Christmas Day. I went in a wheelchair but the nostalgia which surrounds our family home at Wigborough Manor drained me of emotion and Peggy and I retreated home rather quickly.

Early in January 1987 I started therapy of a different nature with a weekly visit to the Apollo Club at Sherborne. This is a special club which meets on Tuesday evenings at the swimming pool hired from Sherborne School. It enables those who may be handicapped in any way to enjoy themselves in a full-sized swimming pool.

The disabilities may be of a physical nature such as my own or people with other problems such as Downs Syndrome or permanent physical damage caused by accidents. A great deal of help is given by people either in the water, at the pool-side or on the administrative side of things. We normally had as many as sixty people including helpers, actually in the water and six people round the baths ensuring that the swimmers were safe at all times.

When my visits started, the weather outside was frosty, the atmosphere was damp and the pool appeared to be very large and the water very deep. I was helped to change into my normal swimming gear, using my walking stick and led to the pool side. I was very nervous about getting into the pool.

However, strong arms lifted me down into what seemed only lukewarm water. I have since discovered the temperature in the pool is never below 75°F.

I was helped to walk across the pool and back again three times. The walking was very laboured and very tiring. I was lifted, exhausted, from the water. Back in the changing rooms, I had a warm shower before being dressed by a marvellous carer. I had been there for just half an hour and departed exhausted and somewhat dispirited.

Peggy drove me home and I was in bed by nine o'clock. I was glad to lie back on my three pillows which supported my unbalanced torso and thankful to have a metal cage over my feet to prevent the bedclothes pressing too tightly on my spastic foot.

In spite of this early frightening experience, I was resolved to keep up the good work of swimming as I had read and heard of the great benefits derived from full immersion in water. For some weeks, I gained little confidence when trying anything away from the immediate support of my two helpers and felt physically weakened.

Eventually after some weeks of trying to walk unaided across the baths at a depth of about five feet, the buoyancy of the water and the return of my confidence in my own ability led me to attempt more agile exercise which led to some form of swimming.

I had never been a strong swimmer but have found much pleasure in this type of therapy. I cannot swim in the usual way face downwards because my sense of balance has been severely impaired and I have always to swim on my back. I have neck and arm floats to assist me.

I had to have two helpers when swimming, one to keep my head on even keel, the other to assist my right leg and right arm. When moving through the water, the helper gave encouragement to the right leg and right arm often speaking quite loudly and the brain responded to those instructions. At first all these activities required complete concentration to achieve a few back strokes. Now I can manage to swim with assistance as much as twenty lengths of the baths.

This perseverance and doggedness plus a little cussedness led me to receive an award from the club at Sherborne. I was awarded an International Swimming Teachers Association Swimming Award for endeavour and the badge has been displayed on my swimming trunks to give me a reminder that hard work even when one is confronted with hardship is rewarded by people who may be fit. The badge was given in September 1987 at which time, I was able to swim unaided and unsupported one length of the baths.

My pleasures were increased by an invitation from one of our swimming club helpers to propose a toast for the club at our Annual Dinner. Public speaking has always been a particular favourite of mine but my confidence had been severely dented by the stroke. To be asked to do this task even amongst friends and not before a critical audience, I felt was a challenge. I accepted the invitation but not without some foreboding. This event took place in March 1988. It was an important step in my recovery as I felt an immediate return of some confidence.

Peggy and I went to the East Coker Village Hall near Yeovil. There were probably about eighty guests present. Throughout the day I had been rehearsing in my mind what I would say. I felt very nervous. Could I do it? Could I get my tongue round the more difficult words? Would the hesitancy that I know was in my speech become more pronounced?

I was never one for reading prepared speeches. What would I say? After the meal our Chairman, John, proposed the loyal toast to the Queen. Then I was asked to propose a toast to the club.

I stood up. Very nervous. I looked around for two seconds and began. 'Mr Chairman, ladies and gentlemen' (My earliest teaching had insisted on always starting correctly). 'How nice to be here among friends'. Suddenly I realised that the knack of speaking in public had not deserted me. I hadn't stood up and spoken to an audience for a year and nine months. I have always been fond of fun and humour but my speeches have usually been on the serious side. While I wanted to tell a humorous story, I kept to my original idea. My early speech training in the Young Farmers Club movement had told me to 'stand up, speak up and shut up'.

I went on to mention the friendship I had received from the helpers within the Apollo Club. How the camaraderie within the club had rejuvenated my self-confidence and how I looked forward to the future with my morale boosted by just standing up and speaking, even to a small audience.

After a few minutes, I sat down with applause ringing in my ears. I thought 'I've done it'. I'd made a speech to a small audience of perhaps 80 people. From that night forward, I have progressed step by step and now my speech is back to normal, I think.

Swimming is still an important feature of my eventual recovery – the complete relaxation of the body and the body's sense of buoyancy are wonderfully therapeutic. The exercises and challenges given me by my helpers are of immense benefit. I shall continue swimming for a very long time.

Frustration and boredom were relieved by visits three times a week to the physiotherapy department at South Petherton Hospital. Peggy took me for an hour and I went through what seemed endless therapy.

I walked up and down the six yards within the parallel bars for as many times as I could manage. This was to help get my balance and to strengthen my right leg.

A small piece of apparatus was standing against the wall. It had handrails on either side. I had to walk up four steps. Then there was a three foot square platform. I had to turn through ninety degrees. Then I had to walk down three steps.

When going up the steps, there were four. When coming down the other side there were three.

Going upstairs was comparatively (and still is) easy. Coming down, even three steps was much more difficult.

The right foot seemed unattached to the right leg. There seemed to be little control of the right leg.

It took a very long time to strengthen the leg and the foot. Countless hours of exercises at the various physiotherapy departments I've attended. Many miles of walking on roads have gradually strengthened the leg.

My right arm was put into a piece of apparatus which reduced the spasticity. Air was pumped into a rubber sleeve that extended from my right shoulder to my finger tips. When the sleeve was blown up, the pressure on my arm was uniform.

In this way, the spasticity was greatly reduced and the therapist could then give me more advanced normal exercises.

Every afternoon I did ten minutes exercise on the static bicycle. This hard work continued for three months and was an immense benefit.

I started to have occupational therapy at Yeovil Hospital on a weekly basis starting during the first week of October 1986. After an early lunch, I was collected with my wheelchair and transported by ambulance to Yeovil. The sessions were for two hours at first. Eventually I went in the mornings and stayed until 3.30 p.m.

Occupational therapy is a lesser-known facet of treatment compared with physiotherapy. To the stroke patient, it is equally important. Exercises were of two types: light and heavy.

In the light workshop, I made coffee for everyone at 10.30 each morning and tea at 3 o'clock in the afternoon. Afterwards I washed up the cups and saucers and dried the cutlery. I don't suppose anyone who hasn't been through a stroke can understand how a grown man could possibly get a sense of really having achieved something after washing up a sink full of crockery; but I did.

Numerous small objects such as a thimble, a coin, a match – twenty in all – were put into a bowl containing hard grains of rice. The exercise was to pick the objects out of the rice with my right hand.

I played a game of hopscotch with my right leg and right foot. The therapist chalked a two foot square on the floor of the workshop. This square was divided into nine and random numbers were marked out on each square. The exercise was to step accurately into each square.

I was put on an exercise bicycle. Not the normal kind of exercise bike. I was harnessed into a machine with pedals. The cranks above the pedals could be adjusted so that the left leg did nothing whilst the right leg made any propulsion. This was very hard work as the righthand side of my trunk was very rigid and required much exercise to loosen the deep spasticity. The medical bicycle had an enumerator fitted which told me how many revolutions I had made. A record was made and every day had to be a little more.

Of the countless other games and appliances in the workshop none was more useful and stimulating than the computer. It was a very basic machine and has since been updated. Various objects were shown on the screen including a dot which appeared at random intervals and in random places. I had to press a button immediately the spot appeared. At the end of the session, a print-out appeared which gave the reaction times. Practice makes nearly perfect and I was ninety-nine per cent normal in my visual reaction.

I felt elated. Despite the many difficulties that I felt, my reactions were nearly normal. As long as I was looking straight ahead, my eyes could focus.

Perhaps I would soon be able to drive my car again.

Perhaps we would soon be able to go away on holiday.

Perhaps. Perhaps. Perhaps.

At that time, I had not finally accepted that I would not be an active farmer again. Perhaps there would be a miracle cure. The realisation of how near death I had been had not yet dawned on me.

The heavy workshop is exactly like a wood workshop at school. There were benches and lathes, power saws and sanders. There was a store room containing many lengths and sizes of timber.

I was never a DIY man. I preferred working with animate objects. Growing things in the fields and gardens. Watching a new life beginning when a cow has her calf.

Trees had been felled to give us timber. They are dead. A calf is alive. It may live for ten years.

My first task in the heavy workshop was making a simple bird table. It hangs in my garden now. Roger, the physiotherapist in the heavy workshop has been my constant companion ever since those days. He gave me early encouragement to write this book and has always given me great help. I needed twenty pieces of timber of various sizes and shapes to do this job. I couldn't really cut them up. My peripheral vision was seriously impaired when it came to sawing along a straight line. The sessions lasted about an hour in the morning and an hour in the afternoon. I was very tired at the end of the afternoon. Perhaps I had been able to prepare only three or four pieces of timber. Painting the finished work was somewhat easier as I only required one hand.

It took about eight weeks to complete. They were eight weeks of considerable effort. But I did it, and at Christmas time I brought home my handywork. Proud as punch. I really had achieved something.

In 1987, I went on to attempt more constructive work in the carpentry shop. I looked at various catalogues to see simple wooden toys I could make.

One of the physiotherapists at South Petherton Hospital suggested I could make a rocking horse for the department. When mothers come to have treatment, their children could use the horse. I thought this was a very good idea.

The making of the horse was good therapy. It would be put to good use as well.

It took about twelve weeks to construct. The runners had to be cut out and prepared accurately. Similarly the legs and seat. Doing the head was more difficult.

I was never one for doing a second-rate job. The planing and sawing had to be accurate. The various pieces were then screwed together. By me, I might add.

Finally there was the varnish and the leather on the seat.

As part of my therapy we invited various friends to two supper parties and we included members of the physiotherapy department. I was very pleased and proud to present the rocking horse to Julia. Since that time, she has had her first baby. The rocking horse is hers and her child's. I hope it gives them as much pleasure to use as I had in making it.

Having completed one, I then made two more for my own grandchildren. At the time there were just two of them, although since then there have been another three.

Between the occupational therapy department and physiotherapy department there was a different kind of attitude. In the physiotherapy department there was a more clinical outlook on life. A person has broken a leg or an arm. The limb needs strengthening through exercises or manipulation.

Occupational therapy is much more subtle. You are a person not a patient. A person who is disabled in body only. Many men and women are disabled in mind, many suffering from depression.

I was always working alongside friends and equals. This definitely gave my morale a boost.

Laughter has always been known as a great healer. Frank had a very bad car accident. He had multiple injuries to his legs and arms. He had a marvellous sense of humour. We had a great repartee between us. He was the funny man with the dead pan face. I was always the 'fall guy'; a latter day Laurel and Hardy act in a way.

I rarely missed the hospital taxi at 9 o'clock in the morning. I was very tired by midday and always had a sleep on a bed in an ante-room in the occupational therapy department to recharge the batteries. Therapy finished at 3.30 in the afternoon and I was brought home, tired out and weary.

This routine of therapy continued unabated throughout 1987. All the time I was making very slow but steady progress along the depressingly long road to recovery.

This professional therapy, however, only occupied my

aching and frustrated body for twenty-five per cent of its time. What could I do with the rest of my time?

The early days after I returned home were ones of confusion, frustration, anger and depression. What did the future hold for me? No more being the one out in front. No more travelling in the fast lane.

Why did I have a stroke? Perhaps those sudden headaches I had had over many years had been a warning. They had lasted perhaps thirty seconds. I had a sudden pressure within my head. Sometimes it happened when working, sometimes when I was bendingover. Once when sitting talking to my uncle one Sunday evening.

They were warning signals. I paid no heed to them. I was strong enough to overcome such little discomforts.

Perhaps though, the stroke, distressing as it has been, may have released one character. In its place is a new personality.

5

A SET BACK AND A REPRIEVE

Unfortunately the road to recovery has been strewn with setbacks. These setbacks had an unintentional air about them. In February 1987 my medical advisers felt that I should go to Frenchay Hospital at Bristol to be assessed by experts there. Peggy took me by car to the Hospital on the Monday before Easter. I was not confined to bed but underwent many tests over the next three days and assessments from various doctors and therapists.

I received a complete body scan in their very sophisticated unit. I was required to lie down, fully clothed, on a hospital bed and a tunnel of various dials enveloped but never touched me. By remaining motionless whilst the tunnel rotated slowly round me a recording was made of the various body signals and signs whilst the machine was in operation. At the same time as the machine was rotating an X-ray picture was being taken at regular intervals throughout the length of the body. This provided the doctors with a picture of any damage which had been done inside the head and throughout the trunk, arms and legs.

There were the inevitable tests of my reflexes by the use of the patella hammer on my right leg and right arm. This showed that some reaction was present and gave me some encouragement. Tests were also done to the soles of my feet to ensure that feeling was present.

I was seated on a fairly firm bench and the physiotherapist measured my reactions by attempting to unbalance me from a normal sitting posture. This was done either by forcing my shoulders from side to side or by forcing my trunk backwards and forwards.

An assessment of my mental capabilities was made at various times throughout my stay. This took the form of reading passages from a book, handling money, and playing various games. Numerous blood samples were taken and various medical staff carried out interviews. It was not possible for me to know the exact purpose for which these had been performed. The food was passably good.

On the Wednesday afternoon, I was told that the chief specialist would be visiting the ward on the Thursday. Thus began the long hours of waiting for him to come and hoping that he would say that I would make a full recovery.

Eventually he arrived in the ward about 12.30 p.m. He had a full retinue of acolytes, junior doctors, student medics and his own personal secretary. He had undoubtedly read all my notes and heard from his deputies of their assessments of my various capabilities. He spent a few minutes explaining in medical terms his assessment of the situation.

The 64,000 dollar question came when I asked him
'what can I do now doctor?' and
'when will I recover?'
A direct question requiring a direct answer.
His reply came like a bombshell.
He said 'Do the best you can but I doubt that you will ever be any better'.
I was devastated. I had to hold back my tears. The scrap-heap can best describe the place where I felt I needed to be. All I wanted to do was go home, to be

with my wife who knew everything.

What the medical people didn't know was the character of the man. The determination and dedication of one man to overcome the difficulties of life after a stroke.

The journey home from Bristol seemed endless in spite of knowing it well. I soon retired to bed and cried myself to sleep.

Next day, Good Friday, I felt very morose and dispirited.

How was I to cope with anything?

I couldn't cut up my food,

I couldn't write a letter in spite of my ability to comprehend,

I couldn't drive a car,

I couldn't be separated from my carers to buy a newspaper at the shop or go to the bank.

Going on a bus or walking other than in our private drive was completely out of the question.

There seemed to be many insurmountable obstacles and the melancholy I felt soon welled over into uncontrolled tears. The doctor had to be called and he prescribed a return to some anti-depressant drugs. The use of valium had been suddenly stopped when I was in Frenchay Hospital. This had resulted in severe withdrawal symptoms.

Peggy consulted our doctor and between them they advised gradual withdraw of valium over a period of about three months. This was most effective and valium is not now taken.

Peggy and I celebrated our Easter Communion in our own home and the occasion saddened me as for the second time a great Christian Festival passed without us being able to join our many friends in the joys of the occasion.

However the sadness of Easter Day quickly passed as

the Bank Holiday Monday dawned. It was a glorious spring morning with warm sunshine and balmy air. Good friends joined us for an al fresco lunch on our own back lawn.

I felt the routine of physiotherapy, occupational therapy, swimming, being taken to hospital by an ambulance service, and being brought home again, playing Scrabble regularly at eleven a.m. on Tuesday mornings and Thursday mornings – this continual chain of mediocrity had to be broken somehow. Plenty of people came to see me but I couldn't get out of my trap and visit other people.

By this time, I realised I would never return to my former work as a practical farmer. Maybe I should be able to give some advice and lend my name to any financial transactions.

This period of deep depression was a turning point upon the long road to my eventual recovery. I felt I had to use some form of latent talent which seemed to want to be released from my confused mind. The beautiful Somerset countryside awakened some hidden desires in my body which was only half in use but my mind had all its senses. I felt my experiences since my stroke might act as a therapeutic pick-me-up.

I decided I would try this writing. My earliest sorties were very uncoordinated. They were slow in execution but hurried in thought. Those early passages were loosely and incoherently written.

After many copies had been written and discarded I eventually found a form of words which seemed to cover my innermost feelings.

An article was written for the *Hope Magazine*, a quarterly publication of the Chest, Heart and Stroke Organisation. This is devoted to patients who have problems associated with high blood pressure and strokes. The article was accepted by the editor and published in the autumn issue of 1987.

The summer of 1987 saw some slow improvement in my physical condition. I seemed to have reached a plateau of seeming mediocrity. I was still very frustrated. I cried frequently as a form of release from the depression I felt. In August my therapist at Yeovil Hospital considered it was safe for me to travel by ordinary bus. Peggy transported me to the village and I got the bus to Yeovil.

For the first time I was alone. Alone and by myself. I was travelling along a familiar road, a road I had known all my life. Our school bus had used it every day. People got on. They didn't look at me. I was just another person. My stick rested beside me.

There weren't many people on the bus. No one spoke to me. More people got on. When we arrived at Yeovil, the bus was half full of passengers. The bus stop was very close to the hospital. A few people got off. Then it was my turn. I stepped down to the pavement and the bus drove off.

There I was. Alone. On a pavement. There were no friends in sight. I was very nervous. The walk to the hospital was no more than one hundred yards. There was nobody to support me. What should I do if I fell over?

I felt so exposed. Would I be beaten up? I had no protection. For fifteen months I had been protected physically. I had to learn to stand on my own two feet. Maybe I couldn't stand properly. But stand I had to.

I walked less than forty yards on a wide pavement fearful that I should be pushed over. There seemed to be nobody there who might help me if I fell down. Then there was a wide pathway at the side of the hospital. It was slightly uphill but without steps. Then there was a level pavement alongside the wall of the hospital. The total distance of my first, unaccompanied, walk was barely one hundred yards. It took me ten minutes to negotiate it.

When I arrived in the therapy department that morning, I was sweating with fear maybe, certainly apprehension. But again, my disabled body had overcome a small but significant obstacle.

At the same time as this great adventure a super surprise came my way. A fellow stroke patient at Yeovil Hospital and I were sent to Exeter for assessment of our capabilities of driving a car again.

An MOT advanced approved instructor sat me in the driver's seat of his own adapted car. He asked me lots of question about myself – how long had I been driving? Had I ever had an accident? What kind of vehicles had I driven?

We then set off on a driving circuit. At the time it seemed the whole circuit but the distance travelled was less than one hundred yards. This was within the confined space of a private car park. The experience, however, gave my morale a boost. Some form of normality began to beckon. Half an hour of questioning and driving ended with the instructor saying that in his own opinion that with good familiarisation from an approved instructor, I should be able to drive again.

Then began weeks of waiting for official notification from the Department of Transport in Swansea that they would give me permission to drive a car. I had to surrender my old licence, which I had had since 1944. I had certain medical tests given by an independent doctor, who had been appointed by the Department of Transport. At the end of September 1987 all the work seemed to be completed and I was officially told I could drive a car on the road again.

I had always been in the driver's seat since I started

driving on June 30th 1945. That was my seventeenth birthday. As testing of drivers had been abandoned in the war years, I had never passed a test.

I had been able to drive for 15,330 days. Suddenly it had stopped and I had been relegated to a passenger, a second-class citizen as far as I was concerned.

No more. This, the worst form of disability, was nearly over.

I then had to take my adapted Volvo 343 car on the public road for the first time. It was a very frightening and traumatic experience. The car was fully automatic with two modifications. The accelerator had been adapted for my left foot to do any operations that are necessary. On the steering column, an extension had been fitted to the windscreen wiper lever so that I can operate this with my left hand.

An advanced driving school instructor came to give me a lesson at 8.30 one morning. He gave me brief instructions on how to handle an automatic car. Although I had never taken an official test, I was reminded of some of the basic rules of the Highway Code. We then started actually driving the car with me in the driver's seat.

I drove at fifteen miles an hour along the 375-yard private drive that led to the public road. The moment of truth had arrived.

Would I be able to negotiate the double bends which are one hundred yards from the farm entrance?

Would I be able to keep in to allow other vehicles to approach and pass my car?

Would I be able to negotiate the right-angled bends before entering the village?

Would the pedestrians walking on the pavement outside the shops step off into my path and cause an accident?

We made off for the main A303 road. It was a very

busy single carriageway road with cars and lorries continually passing each other. On the dual carriageway sections, they speed at seventy to eighty miles an hour. I drove for five miles on the A303 before turning to head for Yeovil. My instructor encouraged me to drive a little faster – my speed having been only twenty miles per hour!

I was required to negotiate a roundabout before returning the way I had come. It was a very difficult manoeuvre. The steering wheel had to be turned almost full circle. My right hand, my right leg, my right trunk could give no assistance to my left hand. The instructor saw my difficulties and assisted me out of my anxiety. I returned to the farm, a little more confident, but, still very nervous. The lesson had lasted for one hour. I had driven, I HAD DRIVEN a distance of twenty miles. It was an achievement I had accomplished on my own.

It was the next step, a very important step on my path to recovery. The next day I had a second lesson when my instructor said he thought I could negotiate in town traffic. It was a hair-raising experience. There were many cars and buses and long articulated lorries. I had to negotiate many roundabouts. It seems stupid now, but at the time it was very frightening, especially on the return journey. My instructor sat in the back seat of the car and never said a word. By the time we returned to the farm I was completely exhausted. But every black cloud has a silver lining.

I paid for my lessons and asked the instructor for my next appointment. 'I shan't want to see you again' was the reply 'you're quite capable of driving your own car.' This was a great surprise but I was filled with a little apprehension. I felt great emotion at being given this reward for what I felt was much hard work. I cried with relief that I had overcome a great barrier which seemed to confront me.

The next day I drove the ten miles to Yeovil Hospital and since that time my self-confidence has gradually returned. I have driven many miles since and driven many people, driven on motorways at a speed of seventy miles per hour, driven in many conditions and all without fear and without other road users causing an accident. Driving the car has given my morale a tremendous boost.

In September 1987, my therapists at Yeovil District Hospital carried out their usual three-monthly assessment of my progress. I was responding slowly to all the exercises and advice I had been given. I had been one hundred per cent dependent at the time of the stroke on treatment from the therapists. The situation was changing as they had predicted. I was depending less on my professional carers and more on my own resourcefulness and enterprise. Throughout the autumn months I was conscious that I should soon be wholly dependent on my own initiative to take my place in the community. Not as before. Not as a practical farmer, working from six thirty every morning to nine or ten at night. But what could I do? I had done some woodworking as part of my occupational therapy at Yeovil Hospital. This seemed rather mundane and didn't satisfy my fertile brain. Why not write a book about a stroke? And so began the first tenuous steps along the path of putting pen to paper and recounting the trials and tribulations of a stroke patient.

My first attempts were very disjointed, hastily composed and very amateurish. My only ambition was to get to the end of the book. The stroke patient has always to get to the end of anything. Whether it is reading an article in the daily newspaper or listening to a play on the radio. It seems there is always some unfinished business to attend to.

By Christmas 1987, I had written seven thousand words and gave it to a friend who was in the publishing world in London. Peter read this manuscript and encouraged me to develop the story further.

In the autumn of 1987 I returned to my great pastime as a member of the South Petherton Combined Arts Society Choir. This has grown from a small group in 1947 of nine sopranos, five altos, five tenors and five basses and conductor to a choir now of over sixty members, with about twenty sopranos, twenty altos, eight tenors and fifteen basses. Ann Willy has been our conductor since 1950 and has inspired and encouraged singers of all ages to contribute to the high esteem in which the choir is recognised in the district. I cannot read music in the normal way. I have to learn my music by ear. Its therapeutic value has been tremendous to me.

The choir performed Stainer's '*Crucifixion*' in 1962 when I was first a member. In 1963 we sang Faure's *Requiem* in the Parish Church at South Petherton. It was a quite marvellous sound. It is still my favourite composition. In the intervening years the choir has sung many favourite oratorios including Handel's *Messiah*, Mendelssohn's *Elijah*, Haydn's *Creation* and various works by Mozart, Verdi, Bach, Arthur Somervell and Vaughan Williams.

My return to the bass section gave me great pleasure. All the members gave me valuable support. To sing correctly, I had to breathe correctly . Practices always begin with breathing exercises. I had to stand up and expand my chest so that I could sing simple phrases.

I found I was becoming out of breath. I hadn't sung in the choir for eighteen months. Would my voice be able to sing in tune?

I couldn't read the music very easily because I couldn't hold any book. I couldn't turn over the pages.

I can't read music anyway. So I had to hear the notes. I don't know and never will know the difference between a C natural and D natural.

I got over the difficulties of holding the music by having a music stand at subsequent rehearsals. I found difficulty in standing through a whole rehearsal. But I found I was able to listen to the music and learn it by ear.

Although there were what seemed insurmountable obstacles, I persevered because I felt singing was a good form of therapy. To be surrounded by the choir at rehearsals lifted my flagging soul onto another plane.

I was back as a member of society and I hope I shall continue singing with the South Petherton Combined Arts Choir for many years.

In October 1987, Peggy and I took our first holiday together since my stroke. We spent three glorious days at Salcombe with two other couples. The weather was perfect, the views from the chalet were quite breathtaking and the company was very conducive to good conversation. These friends were keen bridge players and they reintroduced me to playing bridge. I had not played since my days at college and was very rusty. My nervousness soon disappeared and the cut and thrust of the game seemed to excite my competitive spirit. At the end of the first evening, honours were even and I felt equal to playing further games. I now play regularly at least once a week and would play once a day if anybody would give me a game!

As the Christmas season approached it was plainly obvious that my treatment at Yeovil Hospital was soon to finish. There was a marked running down of interest in what I was doing. I finished my treatment at the time of the Christmas party. I had had excellent treatment throughout my fifteen months in the physiotherapy and occupational therapy departments of Yeovil Hospital. Laughter had been, as always, a valuable medicine and staff and patients have always taken the same attitude.

The exercises which I had been doing were then to be finished.

No more rolling on my back with an eight inch rubber ball beneath the base of my spine. This had been designed to help my spastic leg.

No more kneeling on a rubber mat or moving a three-foot rubber ball with my right hand. This exercise was for releasing my right hand from the tightness caused by the lack of feeling in my limbs.

When the Christmas party at the hospital was concluded I took home with me the two rocking horses which had been made for my two grandchildren. I was sorry to be leaving my many friends who had been so kind to me over the months but glad to be taking home some real achievements – my Christmas presents for my grandchildren. When the festive season was over and all the excitement of my new-found freedom had begun to evaporate I felt somewhat lost.

What could I do? One thing I was going to do was to carry on with the book I had written about my stroke. One of the aims in writing the book was to try and answer the question of why I had suffered a massive stroke.

Medical opinion is somewhat divided on the reasons for a cardio-vascular accident. High blood pressure is undoubtedly one reason.

I had been a blood donor for many years but had been advised by the doctors at the National Blood Transfusion service to see my own doctor in 1984 when I went to give one of my twice-yearly blood donations. I was told my blood pressure was a little high and two tablets per day were prescribed for the rest of my life.

I had smoked cigarettes when I was a younger man but had given up the habit due to a heavy cold soon after I was married. I had however started smoking small cigars in 1976 when I felt under some tension when waiting to take part in a TV programme. The cigar smoking habit had increased to fifteen or twenty per day although I have naturally stopped smoking now.

But what about the stress? When did it start? My whole life has been stressful. I had been bullied and ridiculed at a very early age. The Cancerean character is extremely sensitive.

The more I thought about it, the more I realised that the original causes of this stress lay right back in the earliest part of my life. Perhaps this would be the right point to go back and consider this important aspect of my story.

6

WHERE IT ALL BEGAN – WARTS AND ALL

I was born on June 30th, 1928 at Rydon Farm, South Petherton. My father was Donald Joseph, the third son of Joseph Gladstone and Ellen Mary Vaux. He was born at the turn of the last century on June 27th 1900. With his elder brothers Sydney and Jack, who were fellow farmers, and his younger brother, Harold, who became a leading motor engineer with Alvis Ltd and Armstrong Siddeley Ltd, he was brought up in the true Victorian fashion. Father was always head of the house and his word was law and had to be obeyed.

My mother Hilda Annie was the product of a rather different type of parent. Richard and Ursula Tucker, my maternal grandparents, came from Bideford, North Devon in 1921. Their other children were Arthur (Uncle Ar) who became my mentor until his death in 1978, and another child, Greta, who died of pneumonia soon after they arrived in Somerset.

Hilda was a lovable character who always obeyed her husband. In those days, women did just that – obeyed, come hell or high water.

My brother, John, was born in August 1930, my sister, Nina, in June 1933 and another brother, Geoffrey in January 1938. He was delicate and died of pneumonia in February 1939.

Life in the farmhouse and on the farm was vastly different from today. There was no electricity in the house until connected in 1932. Mains water supply had just been connected in 1927. There were only two carpet squares in the house. These were in my parents' bedroom and in the sitting room. The rest of the house had linoleum on the floor with rugs beside the bed.

I went to bed by candlelight until I was four years old. TV was beyond the imagination of the ordinary person. Radio was still very much in its infancy. We had only a battery-operated wireless set.

It was not all plain sailing. I was not blessed with the best of good looks. I had a broad head for one so young. My hair was very straight and without the vestige of a curl.

I was a very sensitive child. Something to do with the Cancerian make-up. My father and his brothers constantly teased me about my indifferent looks.

'Why didn't I have curly hair like my brother'.

'I'll knock your bullet head off those shoulders'.

Those were some of the jibes I had to endure as a child.

One vivid incident sticks in my memory to this day. I saw a rabbit in the garden and tried to catch it. One of my uncles and my father told me to 'get some salt and put it on the rabbit's tail'.

Childlike, I did as I was told. I fetched the salt cellar and started looking for the rabbit. It was nowhere to be seen. My father and his brother laughed very loudly and I cried bitterly.

Fifty odd years separates that day from this but I have never completely wiped out the memory.

Another incident is fondly remembered. My mother was helping my father with the haymaking. One evening she was doing some horse-raking in the hayfield alongside the brook when the mist started rising very early, about

7 p.m. This was a field that was about a quarter of a mile long. She and the horse became enveloped in the fog and couldn't be found for a long time.

My father had to get a group of men to search for her in case she had driven into the brook. She was eventually found, safe and well, but I thought I had lost her forever. I was about five years old at the time.

It was an incident that could have been quickly forgotten. But the Cancerian character stores sensitive incidents for a very long time. It was just another niggle in the otherwise plain character.

My school days at the local church school attached to the Church of St Peter and St Paul, South Petherton, are remembered with affection. I was taken to the Post Office to buy my first National Savings Certificate when I was five years old. It cost fifteen shillings or seventy five pence!

I went to the junior school when I was seven and had to stand on my own two feet in the school playground. I was rather small for my age and was constantly bullied.

This bullying stopped abruptly when I was seriously injured in a car accident. On April 30th 1936 we boys had been very noisy during lessons. In consequence, our mistress, Miss Knagg, kept us in the classroom at dinner time until we behaved ourselves.

We were eventually allowed out, one at a time to go for our dinner. I came out of the class behind Eddie Patten. He crossed over the road twenty yards in front of me. I was trying to catch him up. A Shell Mex petrol lorry was coming from one direction. I didn't look the other way and bang! A car driven by an unaccompanied learner driver had knocked me down.

I was knocked unconscious for some minutes. I had a compound fracture of my left femur. My head and face were badly cut and bruised. To make matters worse, I was put in the back of the car with my left leg dangling with the two bones sticking out of the skin.

I went into Yeovil Hospital and after two operations, I was allowed home on June 29th, the day before my eighth birthday. I had a splint around my left leg for six months. I walked with the aid of crutches for over two months.

There is a vivid memory of that occasion and of a happy one that followed it. For my birthday, I was given two Dorset Horn ewes and four lambs as a present. From that day onwards, sheep became an abiding interest with me – their habits and food, their economic importance and their place for centuries in the rural economy of the district.

I went to a private preparatory school in Yeovil from September 1936 until June 1940. I couldn't play rugby and cricket very easily because of my leg. A bad cut in the palm of my right hand made catching a hard cricket ball very painful.

I dropped the catches which most boys would have found quite easy. The sports master christened me 'Butterfingers'. To me he appeared to be a big bully with a vicious 'hand off' when playing rugby, sometimes he was running straight at me.

I went to Yeovil School when I was twelve and I retain many happy memories of those days. Many school activities were seriously curtailed because of the war conditions. There were no outings to view historic places and sporting activities for example. There were however two incidents that had a rather harsh note to them.

Our Headmaster, the late Reverend J W Pearson, had all the characteristics of a strict disciplinarian. He was over six feet tall with a tall dome to his bald head. Not only was the head bald but the blood vessels on his head and face were very close to the surface of his skin and many were ruptured due to a heavy smoker's cough. He was a heavy pipe smoker.

These were but the start of his harsh appearance. He also had a squint. Not a squint in one eye, but a squint in both eyes. You never knew which way he was looking.

One morning I was acting as blackboard monitor. I was cleaning off the blackboard when I was hit behind the ear by a piece of chalk thrown by another boy, Jessie James. I turned round and was just about to throw the duster at Jessie when the 'boss' walked by the classroom. I had been caught in the act! Feeling very small, I went back to my desk deeply embarrassed.

One serious incident is remembered by all who were at the school at the time. There had been some bullying of a small boy in the biology laboratory during one dinner time. The boy had been held over the gas taps for some time. He went blue in the face and was very distressed. The culprits, Messrs Bowser, Whitby, Pring and Sharman, were given six strokes of the headmaster's cane next morning. These were big boys but the cane was brought down hard upon the backside of all four. The school was in a very subdued state for several days.

I gained my school certificate and was exempted from the matriculation examination at the age of fifteen. I had credits in English Language, French, History, Chemistry, Maths and General Science. My favourite subjects were English Literature and Geography. I spent too much time answering the questions on *Farmers Glory* by A G Street and didn't finish the paper properly. The questions about the coalfields of Wales and the woollen and cotton mills of Yorkshire and Lancashire again were answered too fully. In these subjects I didn't obtain a credit, just a pass mark. In art, I failed.

During the autumn and spring terms of 1943–44, I had numerous colds and flu, due to being in and out of classrooms all the time. I was going to leave school at sixteen but my father persuaded the Headmaster that my health was more important and I could do some useful work upon my uncle's farm rather than continue for one term at school. I left school in March 1944, aged fifteen and three-quarters.

For the next eighteen months I worked very hard and very willingly for my uncle, Arthur Tucker and his wife Doris at Castle Farm, Ilchester, near Yeovil. Much of my basic training in agriculture was learnt from him. I learnt how to milk cows by machine and clean out the muck from the cow stalls. This muck was loaded into horse-drawn carts and deposited in the field and spread by hand at a later stage.

There was a large herd of pigs which were fed upon the swill collected from the nearby Royal Naval Air Station at Yeovilton. This was a stinking, filthy, greasy, job which I was daily involved in for eighteen months, first as a driver's mate, then, when I was seventeen, as a driver of a converted Standard car. It had its back seat and the rear half of its chassis removed and the rear axle brought forward. This enabled an otherwise small horse-powered car to pull heavy loads. In the winter time we often collected one and a half tons of swill on Fridays and Saturday mornings.

The swill was cooked on the farm by steam and it gave a completely balanced diet to the fattening pigs. There were never less than 350 pigs on the farm.

Arthur Tucker had another farm at Edbrook, Cannington, near Bridgwater. There he had 150 sows which were kept on a free-range system of management.

I learnt much about pig management; how to handle a sow at parturition; how to catch and hold little pigs for earmarking and castration; how to hunt pigs from the field to the buildings; how to load pigs onto a car trailer or lorry. To the uninitiated, these seem very menial jobs requiring little skill. To Arthur Tucker, they were skilled tasks and I was taught those skills.

The days at Ilchester were filled with work. Arthur Tucker was a great one for the mornings. 'Always be ready at five to seven to meet the men at seven o'clock' he would say.

If he was going to a sheep fair and I wanted to go, he would say 'I shall be ready, shaved and changed in five minutes. If you want to go, be ready before me or else you can stay at home'.

It was very good training and it stood me in good stead throughout my life.

There were two incidents at that time that left a deep impression on me.

I became very friendly with an older boy. I had no experience of sexual relationships between boys and girls. I didn't know anything about homosexuality and I was lonely and very naïve.

Our relationship became even closer and on one evening he made strong sexual advances towards me by placing his hand on my knee. I was very alarmed and frightened. I quickly withdrew and hurried away to my lodgings. I was very confused and perhaps this was my first encounter of a more mature nature. Eventually I cried myself to sleep.

At the opposite end of the sexual spectrum I had another experience fondly remembered. I had been quite friendly with a local girl when I was still at school. The friendship had rather waned since we left school and went our separate ways.

On my seventeenth birthday, I got up at quarter to seven and did my round of swill collection from the camp at Yeovilton. I came in to have my usual breakfast of cereals, fried egg, bacon, bread and potatoes. The letters had arrived and I had numerous cards from my father and mother, brother and sister, and various aunts and uncles.

One card was different. I didn't recognise the writing at first. On the back of the envelope, there were the initials S.W.A.L.K. or sweet words and loving kisses. I knew at once who had sent the card.

I was slightly embarrassed and started blushing in front of my uncle and aunt. I opened the envelope and read the card. My face turned a deep, deep red. I came out in a sweat from head to toe. The young lady (she was eighteen at the time) had offered herself, body and soul! I had only to say where and when and my every desire would be granted!

I retell both these events because, today, they seem quite trivial and unimportant. In 1945, any suggestions that a boy had a relationship, however insignificant it might be, with another person of the same sex was severely frowned upon. I should have been banished from my family for good. So for many years I had this awful feeling of guilt.

This guilt was overlaid with the natural passion a young man of seventeen feels for a warm forward young woman of eighteen. Needless to say, the passion had to be subdued somehow. Hard work was the only remedy available at the time. Today it could have been a different matter. These restrictive covenants of former generations caused me much distress for many years.

I finished my early training in farming to go out into the big wide world in September 1945. Until then I had been cocooned on the straight and narrow path of chapel and family. Now would be my chance to kick over the traces. I could have a good time. I could smoke cigarettes as much as I liked. I could go out with as many girls as I liked. There would be no holds barred.

My father had been a pupil at the College of Agriculture at Reading, which in 1921, was a part of London University. There he obtained a diploma in Dairy Management. The Head of the College had been Professor H G Robinson MA. He later became principal of the farm institute at Sutton Bonington near Loughborough, Leicestershire. In 1946 it became the Faculty of Agriculture of Nottingham University.

Getting places at more advanced seats of learning was very difficult at the end of the War. For once my father's connections were of great use. His connections with Professor Robinson and his influences in the dairy industry ensured a place for me at Sutton Bonington. I obtained a scholarship from the United Dairies Scholarship Fund, thanks to my father's great work for the Wilts United Dairies and the Milk Marketing Board.

I started at college in September 1945 full of excitement, eager for adventure and raring to go in the new found world of freedom. Little did I know the pitfalls to come. I was brought down to earth with a big bump very quickly.

I was obviously a very brash young man with oafish ways and a very broad Somerset accent. I tended to dress in somewhat flamboyant clothes. I was to put it mildly, a bit of a swank.

One evening I was set upon by a bunch of second year students and de-bagged. Not just de-bagged but much black shoe polish was applied to my bare backside and very firmly and vigorously polished in. To round off the indignity, my trousers were pulled up and I was forcibly put into a cold bath with all my clothes on!!

It was a students' prank designed to 'knock the young bugger off his perch' so I was told. It did just that but I have been the best of friends with the same students to this day. The experience left a deep impression on my otherwise rough exterior.

My days at college were filled with learning and laughing. I took external exams at Leeds University and gained a National Diploma in Agriculture in the summer of 1947.

I was rather small for my age and not a particularly good athlete at rugby, football or cricket. I became the man who acted as trainer or referee, umpire or scorer. In one word, I was known as a dogsbody to the rugby XV or the cricket XI.

I joined the Dramatic Society and appeared in two productions. I played in billiards and snooker competitions and was a member of the table tennis team. I was also a member of the Joint Common Room Committee organising various social activities within the college.

This period away from home amongst young men and women was when I felt released from the family pressures. Within a few days of leaving college in July 1947, I had a great surprise. I had been awarded the Harold Gore-Brown prize. (He was a benefactor of the old County Colleges). This was in recognition of the 'all round service' given to the college in 1945–47. I was very proud as I hadn't even known the prize existed. I had only entered into the spirit of college activities.

The euphoria was quickly destroyed when I went to work as a third cowman on my uncle's farm at Wigborough Farm, Lower Stratton, South Petherton. Sid and Jack Vaux were of the old school. They were self-made men who had little time for upstarts from college. I could see that much needed to be improved. But I never had a chance to make any changes.

During my first week as an employee, I was literally penniless. I had spent all my savings when I was at college and my father told me 'you can stand on your own two feet now'. On the Wednesday, I was asked to go for a drink with some friends. I had to borrow ten shillings (fifty pence) from my cousin until pay day on Friday. I was crestfallen. Never before and never since have I been so short of money.

My stay at Wigborough Farm was not a particularly happy one. I often cried myself to sleep. There was much improvement that could have been accomplished which I felt equipped to do. However it was not to be and I left in February 1948.

By this time my father's career as a professional organiser was ended. In 1945, he left the Milk Marketing Board to become Organising Secretary of the Somerset National Farmers' Union. There was a clash of personalities and he resigned during the Autumn of 1947. He returned to practical farming on a much reduced scale.

When I joined him in March 1948, his health was not good. He suffered from a grumbling duodenal ulcer. This made him very irritable and we never had a meaningful conversation at any time. We were greatly helped by two German ex-prisoners of war, Willie and Max who lived in a flat over the kitchen until they were repatriated to Western and Eastern Germany in the autumn of 1948.

The main enterprise was strawberry growing. This grew from one acre in 1946 to six acres in 1950. The summers of 1948–49 were very good for strawberries. There was at that time no chemical weed control and I spent weeks hand hoeing in the spring. After the strawberries were harvested, all the straw which had been carefully laid by hand had to be burnt before hoeing started again.

In 1950, the weather completely upset the apple cart. A wet spring meant the weeds were not killed by hoeing. When the straw was put under the berries, the wet conditions encouraged botrytis in the strawberries. Then the berries rotted as they ripened and we only harvested forty per cent of the crop.

When picking stopped in about mid-July, it rained again and burning the straw was impossible. We tried to grow strawberries once more in 1951 but with the same result and after that we abandoned this crop.

7

A LIGHT APPEARS BUT DARK CLOUDS CONTINUE

At this point, I would like to introduce the most important person in my life – my wife Peggy. Originally we had first met when I was fourteen and she was thirteen. She had come to my home as a member of the Junior Ilminster Young Farmers' Club quiz team.

There had been a three-way competition between Martock (of which I was a member) Crewkerne, our arch rivals, and Ilminster.

My initial interest in Peggy turned to more fervent desires by the time I was twenty-one. We courted for a year and became officially engaged at Christmas 1950.

Our wedding day was on December 28th 1951. Most people have only happy memories of their wedding day, ours had to be different. First it poured with rain. It rained so hard about two o'clock that it was impossible to take any photographs outside the church after Peggy and I had married. It went on raining all the afternoon and when we were ready to leave the wedding reception, it was raining so hard no one came to wave us goodbye outside the hall.

There was the inevitable throwing of confetti and rice inside the hall. Much horseplay ensued in which my uncles and my father were involved. In the general melée, Peggy dropped her handbag containing a new powder compact. The mirror was smashed to smithereens. The events of the next seven years may have been foretold in this event as the old superstition says, 'to break a mirror, brings 7 years bad luck.'

Our journey to Tewkesbury that evening and our eventual destination, Keswick in the Lake District, was shocking. Because of the severe south westerly gale, we took more than four hours to reach Tewkesbury. Next morning we awoke to find the town surrounded by flood water. The A38 road north was just passable.

We reached the Lake District in the early evening to be greeted by snow. During the next two days it snowed quite hard. Being southerners, we hadn't brought any chains or ropes. Fortunately there was a slight thaw over the next few days though driving a small Morris eight in the steep passes of the Lake District was never easy.

We stayed a week in Keswick and returned home via two nights in Cambridge and two with friends in Hertfordshire. On Friday January 11th we reached home. My mother's arms were open but not my father's. My mother was crying loudly: 'Father is very ill. He has been in very great pain for several hours.

What a homecoming! The doctor had been called and was coming again at six o'clock. At six, he seemed a little better and we thought that the pain was subsiding. My mother was preparing a roast chicken for the family meal. About seven thirty, the pain became more intense.

The doctor was called again and my father was sent to Yeovil District Hospital. The ambulance came about eight o'clock. I was beside him all the time. During the journey to Yeovil, he was in great pain. He cried bitterly. He put his arms around my neck and said, 'I've had enough, son'.

(There seems a strange similarity between this journey with my own father's cry for pity, and my own journey to hospital and my sinking into the depths of despair).

In that fleeting moment, the Victorian veil was dropped and beneath it was a real man, a man without any defence, a man who was humbled by pain.

I never had that homecoming meal of roast chicken! Next morning I had to be on parade as head of the business at 6.45 a.m. There was no getting out of that particular job. Father underwent an operation to patch up a burst ulcer. When the ulcer had burst, his whole abdomen became poisoned. He became gravely ill and was on the danger list for six weeks. He became semi-conscious and a rota of people had to be found who would sit by his bedside and get him to drink. It was mostly Lucozade, as his kidneys were not working normally.

He was allowed home after three months. He was patched up before the scarred duodenal tissue was ready for removal in August. He came out from hospital at the end of September. He was a spent force. He never did much physical work thereafter. But he could criticise and he could smoke thirty cigarettes a day and he always had enough energy to do anything that the village activities required.

When he came out of hospital I drove him round our smallholding to look at the various crops. I had worked very hard for nine months and was expecting some praise. Instead there was nothing but criticism; why were the crops so dirty and weedy? He didn't realise that we had had a wet September and October.

This uneasiness between us resulted in Peggy and I looking at the possibility of renting several farms. I particularly liked a very good farm at Chedzoy near Bridgwater. Arthur Tucker was quite prepared to support me financially. There were many applicants and I was one of a short list of five. I was placed second because at that time we had no children. The successful candidate was an older man with two teenage sons.

My parents were somewhat relieved that I didn't get the farm. The main driving force in the business was not going away after all.

My disappointment was brought into sharper relief in 1954. I had been made an equal partner in the business in 1952. Suddenly and without any warning or consultation, I was informed that John would also become a partner, which meant that my share of a very small business worth about five thousand pounds, was cut from fifty per cent to thirty three per cent. Our drawings were cut by 25% per month. A bitter pill to swallow especially as our first child, Stephen, had just been born.

However, the business flourished for John and I were always the best of friends. He was a tireless worker. We bought a lorry and marketed much of our produce in Bristol Wholesale Market. We were one of the first vegetable producers to introduce 'facepacks' to cauliflower packing. Six or eight cauliflowers of a similar size, without any blemishes on the curds and all of good colour were selected by eye and placed, curds upwards in wooden crates designed originally to hold a dozen lettuce. Any surplus leaves around the cauliflower were then trimmed off with a sharp butcher's knife. In this way, the buyer could see exactly what he was buying.

At that time all root vegetables were sold as dirty. We started washing root vegetables – parsnips and carrots were our speciality. Everything seemed to be going along quite well.

Fate had the last word however. John had been a member of the drama group of South Petherton Combined Arts Society. He was in a play in December 1959. There was a dress rehearsal on a Tuesday. He complained of a pain in his stomach, but in the best tradition of Thespians 'the show must go on'.

On Thursday he seemed to be slightly better. On the Friday he was again in pain. He played the evening performance with great difficulty but when the final curtain was brought down, he collapsed on the stage.

A doctor was in the audience and immediately called an ambulance. John was taken to Yeovil General Hospital and a burst appendix was diagnosed immediately. He was operated on that evening.

However, peritonitis had set in. Drugs administered in hospital had reacted adversely to antibiotics taken in milk from our own cows. In those days the use of antibiotics to control mastitis in cattle was not fully understood. Our own cows sometimes had mastitis. John was a big milk drinker.

He became gravely ill. Seven different drugs were given in twenty five different combinations. The whole family and the community generally were crestfallen. Prayers were said in church for his recovery. For two or three days his life hung in the balance.

I was at his bedside one evening. I went out for a minute or two to go to the toilet. When I got back, he was out of bed, semi conscious and with sweat pouring from his brow. The depressions around his neck were filled with perspiration. He muttered something about wanting to go home.

Nurses were called and quickly got him back into bed. They viewed the incident with great alarm as seriously ill patients who get out of bed are generally considered to be in a nearly terminal state.

John's wife did the night duty of bedside vigil. Next morning I was on duty. The doctors had a consultation on his condition. One came to me with a piece of paper to sign. 'What's this for?' I asked. 'We've got to operate again. We must open his stomach and let the pus out.

74

We require permission to do this operation. It's our only chance of saving his life'.

It was a terrible decision. Operate and he may just live. Don't operate and he would surely die within twenty-four hours.

There was only one thing I could do. I gave permission. The crisis lasted thirty-six hours. His own great physical strength and endurance pulled him through. He slowly recovered and was out of hospital by the end of February. He was back at work two months later, sadly weakened by his great ordeal. He found the physical side of farming too much for his body. He left practical farming to become the manager of Pershore Growers Depot at West Monkton near Taunton. This again was a big disappointment to me. We were a great team – somewhat short of capital but with tremendous energy and enthusiasm.

In the 1950s, I bought a block of land from other members of the family. It had been used for haymaking and for grazing with sheep. It could be ploughed and vegetable crops would be grown. There was a natural water supply running alongside the land which could be used for irrigation purposes. There was considerable expansion in the vegetable acreage in the late 1950s and early 1960s but again the weather had the final say.

The winter of 1962–63 saw some very heavy snow, more than my father ever remembered in sixty-two years. Snow on December 28th was accompanied by a blizzard. Next morning the snow was twelve inches deep on the fields. Drifts in the gateways and along the sunken roads made driving a car impossible, in fact we never used our car for over a month.

We had no four-wheeled drive vehicle at the time and everything we needed at the farm had to be brought by tractor and trailer. The milk from the dairy had to be hauled across two fields to be collected by our buyer's own vehicles.

The long cold spell until the middle of March played havoc with our plans. The farm's overdraft grew bigger. In 1965 my father officially retired leaving me in sole charge.

In the summer of that year the weather again dealt the body blow. On four occasions between a Monday evening and the following Friday afternoon we had tremendous thunderstorms. An inch of rain fell in an hour, on each occasion. The following Monday we had one and a half inches of rain in twenty-four hours. A total of five and a half inches of rain in a week.

The effect on the farm was devastating. We had just lifted seven acres of early potatoes. The land had been ploughed again and fertilisers had been applied. It was all ready to be planted with winter broccoli.

The three-acre field which was being used to raise all our plants for transplanting purposes was badly infected with club foot or finger and toe disease. This is the scourge of vegetable growers. Once it becomes prevalent in any land, it becomes endemic for seven years at least. No brassica crops can be grown successfully during that time. Erosion occurred on any land which had even a gentle slope. When the gradient was more than one in fifty, the run off of soil, fertiliser and plants was most noticeable.

The business had these difficulties in 1965. They were closely followed by personal disappointment in 1966. Peggy and I were still in bed having a Sunday morning off from work when John and Ruth with their two children, Anne and David, delivered a bombshell.

They had had enough of trying to make a living from farming or the allied industries in this country. They were going to emigrate to Australia. There were many family connections there, particularly in Western Australia. The prospects looked good for a 36-year-old man with no qualifications except for a pleasing manner and good sportsmanship.

They went by boat to Perth, Western Australia in the autumn of 1966. He got a job with Westralian Farmers, Perth in the Jute and Fertiliser Division. This is the biggest farmers co-operative in Australia.

I was very saddened to be losing my best friend and brother. My parents, especially my father, were heart-broken. Gradually his health deteriorated, and in February 1967 he died. He'd had a ruptured spleen brought on by continual coughing as a result of heavy smoking. He had given much service to his fellow men but his life was cut short by ill-health, which was a waste.

During the late 1960s and early 1970s, I saw a large expansion in my vegetable growing enterprise. For several years a big tonnage of carrots was grown for canning. The larger sizes were graded out for use in baby foods. One ton per day was delivered daily to Wells in Somerset. After grading, the carrots were put through a potato scraping machine as used in a fish and chip shop. This was quite a profitable venture.

The smaller carrots went for canning. These were delivered, twenty tons at a time, by lorry to Didcot in Berkshire. The enterprise was mainly profitable. The inevitable squeeze on margins soon ensued. Wages and other costs increased. The buyers increased their prices but not as much as my costs.

Carrot growing was continued for nearly ten years until the large scale production possible in the Eastern counties made it an unprofitable enterprise for us in the West. I learnt that you had to be a grower of at least a hundred acres and near a canning factory.

At that time I became heavily involved in a vegetable marketing co-operative near Exeter. The vegetables were packed exclusively for Marks and Spencer Limited. They were the leaders in quality control. The Devon growers concentrated on growing cabbage, cauliflower, sweetcorn, round lettuce and sprouts. I grew top quality runner beans, cos lettuce, salad onions and sprouts. In the period 1970–1975 I produced forty tons of runner beans per year for pre-packing purposes. Sprouts were produced from mid September to mid March. Over a ton a day was picked and transported to the packhouse at Clyst St Mary.

These ten years were very busy ones. I felt at full stretch. Despite all the problems, age and enthusiasm were on my side. I could work long hours and everything was going well.

Until 1976. Most people remember 1976 as the hot year with temperatures as high as 93°F. The long hot summer meant uninterrupted cricket at the Test Matches. The sun shone continuously but there were some irritating water restrictions for some people. This was the general consensus of opinion.

For me, 1976 was a real disaster. The winter of 1975–76 was mainly dry and mild. There was little or no snow. By April 1st, there was three inches of soil moisture deficit. This official figure indicates that three inches of rain as irrigation must be applied to make most crops grow.

Little rain fell in April and by the end of May, many crops were seriously short of moisture. The effect on my business was catastrophic.

Some sheep had been feeding a short term ley. They were sent home at the end of April. Ploughing the hard ground was very difficult. There was no moisture at all. Sowing the savoy seed was impossible. That twelve acres yielded absolutely nothing.

My staff worked valiantly to establish the twenty-five acres sprout crop. It grew very slowly. Many applications of pesticides were used to control caterpillars and aphids.

When picking started in late September, the sprouts themselves were useless with aphids in the middle, despite the careful treatment. Many acres of the early varieties were abandoned and nothing was harvested at all.

Establishing and growing cauliflower in such hot conditions is very difficult. There was irrigation available in that particular field and I managed to grow a reasonable crop.

The cos lettuce crop was almost a disaster. The crop grew well in the hot, dry spring. There was a good demand from the packhouse. When it came to maturity however, and the crop was ready for cutting, the centre of the lettuce head was found to be unusable. They had 'snotty noses' i.e. the middle of the lettuce just rotted away, due to over heating. I had to abandon three acres.

The hot, dry conditions played havoc with my potato crop. I was growing twenty acres at the time, most of them second early varieties. These were ready for harvesting in July. The crop withered away by the middle of June and many of the potatoes were too small for the market. It was heartbreaking to see tons of little potatoes lying on the ground after harvesting.

There was one crop that did well that year. I had been growing over-wintered Japanese onions for several years. The seed was sown in September and the crop harvested in June and July. Onions like a fairly hot climate.

In 1976, I had seventeen acres. The conditions at harvest time were ideal. The whole crop was sold by the middle of August.

It was not all doom and gloom however in 1976. The National Farmers' Union in Taunton thought it a good idea to give over-wintered Japanese onions a boost.

They produced a press release about the crop, how it was grown and who grew it. There was an immediate response. The *Sunday Times* Business Supplement published a story about the crop and its potential. I had numerous letters from growers both professional and amateur enquiring where they could get some seed. I also had an enquiry from HTV at Bristol.

I told the reporter, Richard, that 'it was too late to see the crop growing' but 'would he like to see the rest of the farm and how badly the drought was affecting it?'

He came down and, after looking around, agreed to send a film crew and a presenter on the second Tuesday in August. It was an ideal day for filming. It was very hot and the crops were shimmering in the sunlight. My female staff – I called them my girls – were wearing bikini tops and shorts. I told the presenter that the public would have to pay dearly for the fine summer. There would be greatly reduced yields of potatoes and the price would increase. There would be poor crops of winter cabbage and all green vegetables during the winter would be most expensive. There would be poor yields of carrots. These were just a few of my comments.

When the programme was ready for transmission on the first Sunday in September, the drought had been broken and we were having quite a lot of heavy rain. The programme made good viewing and was well received by many people.

About a month later, I received a further call from HTV asking if I would like to act as presenter on their West Country Farming programme. Being a publicity conscious person, I agreed. For the next eighteen months, I acted as link man in about twenty farming programmes from Bristol. I was paid for this work but the fees were not excessive.

The terrible growing conditions in 1976 had a serious effect on my cash flow position at the bank. During 1977, I lost several of my employees who had been with me for many years. The high prices received for potatoes and other vegetables in 1976 resulted in a rapid increase in acreage in 1977. Allied with this factor there was a good growing season. A glut of supply ensued followed by the inevitable slump in prices. This was again bad for my cash flow position. My mortgage repayments were not maintained as they should have been.

I had to sell some land to satisfy my mortgagor. It was a sad day. The land was sold at auction and to publicly acknowledge that I had not been able to honour my obligations, was very hurtful.

I made four men redundant and I had to alter course drastically. I had only ninety five acres left. What could we do with those? I say we, because Philip had left college in 1975 and was made an equal partner in 1976.

When I sold the land, inflation had helped increase the cash value considerably. I paid off the mortgagor but there remained a healthy cash profit. Should I simply bank it and pay the resulting tax – over fifteen thousand pounds or invest in some capital project on the farm? I chose the latter and in 1980 we developed a pig fattening enterprise.

We had been privately selling 1,500 ten-week old weaner pigs a year to farmers who merely fattened pigs. We built a specialist fattening house for six hundred pigs. Its design, which was a joint venture, incorporated some important features. Cleaning the muck from any pig house can be a very time consuming job. So mucking out had to be done with a tractor and fore-end loader.

Pigs like a warm bed to lie on and plenty of fresh air in the dunging area. There was plenty of straw to provide insulation above the pigs. At that time skimmed milk was available from cheese factories for feeding the pigs. Our pigs were fed on liquid food consisting of skimmed milk, cereals and minerals.

There were the inevitable swings and roundabouts in

the pig production cycle. The enterprise had one saving grace however. Pigs were always sold, usually about forty five per week. Sometimes the profit margin per pig was not great but the cash flow position was always healthy.

During the 1980s we had a big expansion in our main enterprise. From a very modest output of 250,000 vegetable plants in 1978, we produced in 1986, 12 million vegetable plants and imported 5 million leek plants from Holland. This enterprise was my main work. Ninety per cent of my time was spent thinking about cabbage plant production and working long hours thinking about the best way that I could give good service to my customers.

Our soil and climate were ideal for the purpose, sandy loam soil with no stones and about twenty-five inches of rain per year. We rented twenty-five acres of land from a neighbouring farmer. It suited our requirements admirably. No brassica plants had been grown on his farm for many years and this meant our plants were disease free at all times. There was a good supply of mainly female casual labour from the end of May to the end of October. In fact, in 1985 we had a ninety per cent clearance of all plants.

On reflection the late seventies and eighties were very stressful. I was, as I have said, giving blood at the National Blood Transfusion Centre in South Petherton. I had hoped to collect a medal having given fifty pints of blood over twenty five years. One day I was told I could give blood but I should consult my doctor since my blood pressure was slightly high.

I went to my doctor who told me that my blood pressure was higher than it should be considering my age, height and weight. I should 'take it easy' and he prescribed two tablets a day. When it came to the next blood donating session six months later I had to tell them that I was taking tablets containing Warfarin for my blood pressure. The doctor said 'We cannot take your blood at any time now or in the future.' I was devastated. Gone for good was any chance of that medal. I felt perfectly healthy but the course of tablets has continued and will continue throughout my life.

There were other clouds on the horizon. One day, I was loading one hundred weight sacks of fertilisers with three of my employees. George and I were throwing the bags on to the trailer. Leonard and Stan were handling them on the trailer. It was a hot day and as always, we were in a hurry. George and I bent down to lift up one of the bags. Suddenly I felt dizzy. I didn't fall over. I leant against the side of the trailer. I had to rest my head against my arms. The dizziness soon stopped within thirty seconds. I rested for two or three minutes and thought nothing more about it.

Six months later, exactly the same thing happened again. This time it was rather more serious. I was sitting down talking business to a colleague in my own sitting room. In a few minutes the dizziness passed and I felt fine. These were warning signs and I paid no attention to them.

Christmas 1985 was a happy family occasion. Our eldest son Stephen and his wife Jenny were home with our first grandson Martin. Our other son Philip and his wife Sandra were expecting their first baby in March 1986. When the festivities were over I had to make plans for the plant raising season.

What varieties of Brussels sprouts, cauliflower, cabbage savoy and other brassicas would be grown in 1986? How many hundred thousand of early, mid-season and late varieties? Which seedsman was able to give the best discounted price? The total bill for seed alone was more than £25,000. How much would British Rail charge for haulage? Hundreds of questions all required positive answers.

Then there were the customers. I kept a mailing list and in 1986 sent it to fifteen hundred customers or potential customers. The list had to be constantly updated because of any bad payers. My terms of trading were always strictly payment within twenty-eight days of sending an invoice. A list containing all varieties to be grown, method of growing, delivery charges as well as prices and conditions of payment had been prepared. All the envelopes had been typed and the season was about to start in earnest.

Then a real disaster struck. The weather during February had been cold with little snow. Water pipes were frozen every morning. The first job had to be getting water to all our animals.

On Friday, February 27th there was a particularly hard frost with temperatures as low as $-8°C$. This was accompanied by a strong wind from the north east which meant the chill factor was very intense.

Our employees, Clive, Kerry and Andrew, as well as Philip and myself had to concentrate on getting water and liquid food to all the pigs. All appeared to be going well that morning so I went and had my breakfast at 8.15. I went to Yeovil at 8.45 with my 1500 letters to be posted at the Post Office. I was waiting in the queue to be served when a man appeared from an inner room. 'Is there a Mr Vaux here?'

'Yes', I replied.

'Well you'd better get back to the farm, it's on fire.'

My heart stopped still. I was flabbergasted. What had gone wrong? Was the house on fire or the farm buildings on fire? A dozen questions flashed through my mind in an instant.

I jumped the queue, hurriedly paid my bill and dashed out of the door. I had to drive home as quickly as I possibly could. But I had to avoid as much traffic as possible in the morning rush hour. The horn was blaring all the time and the headlights were full on for the ten-mile journey home. I took the byroads and across the top of Ham Hill, I could see how bad the fire was. A great pall of black smoke could be seen from a distance of three miles away.

When I arrived at the farm, four fire engines were already in attendance. The worst of the flames had already been extinguished. There was still much smouldering wood. Smoke was everywhere. Philip and the men had done a valiant job and saved all the pigs from any injury.

The fire had started in the dry sow pens. A blow lamp had been used to free the frozen pipes. A wisp of loose lighted straw had blown on to the tinder dry straw bales. The wind had done the rest and rapidly fanned the flames.

Within half an hour the dry sow pens which had accommodated twenty five sows and one boar had been completely destroyed. Pens which housed six sows and sixty five piglets were gone completely. The dust from years of pig feeding was smouldering in the tinder dry roof. Many sows and their litters had to be turned out of their pens into the cold yards. Water was everywhere.

There was a risk of explosion in Philip's workshop. He had all our sprays, insecticides and pesticides in the next building. It contained all his workshop equipment including four cylinders of oxygen and acetylene for his welders. Fortunately the sprays were in sealed drums within a heavily wooded cupboard.

By eleven o'clock, the worst was over. Then we had to take stock and sort out where we could house the pigs for a few days. The rest of the day was spent hauling pigs, sows and little pigs to other farms. We had no electricity in the buildings. There was a temporary interruption to the water supply. Philip and the men worked valiantly throughout, although they were completely shattered. During the afternoon, the insurance agent came and quickly gave his verdict. 'You are completely covered. The assessor will be here in the morning to make any judgement'. This reassurance was very helpful and immediately put my mind at rest that there would be no financial loss.

Next morning, three men from a neighbouring farm helped Philip and I prepare a complete list of everything that had been lost or damaged. It took three hours to sift through the blackened remains of the workshop. It was most distressing but it was worth the effort. The value of the equipment was more than fifteen thousand pounds. Then of course there were the buildings on top of that.

The assessor arrived in the afternoon and was full of sympathy. But there was a sting in the tail. When walking across the yard looking at the charred remains of what had been the centre of my whole farm business he said, 'My word is final. You may make what claim you like but my word is law.' I was nonplussed. Surely my insurance company would not have such an assessor with such an arrogant unsympathetic attitude.

I have since learnt that he had cancer of the bowel shortly afterwards. One can make allowances but the incident is not forgotten. The Cancerian never forgets.

With much of our pig housing completely destroyed, quick decisions had to be taken. We had to sell twenty sows and litters in the next three weeks to give us breathing space. Unfortunately the pig trade was in the doldrums. The prices paid were only just passable. The complete loss of the workshop and spray store was a great inconvenience. It meant small poky and old-fashioned buildings had to be used as a temporary measure.

By the middle of March, I was ready for the seed sowing season. I had several million Brussels sprout plants ordered early. The weather was very dull with rain on frequent days. The seed sowing drill worked best in dry weather. The fifteen kilos of sprout seed should have been sown in three days. It took well over a week.

April was rather better. Germination of the early sowings was good. The weather was good and I was able to sow at regular intervals and to my basic plan.

The weather was again very unkind however. In the middle of May, a violent thunderstorm broke about midnight. Two inches of rain fell in four hours. The centre of the storm seemed to be right over the plant field. Next morning I was confronted with a scene of complete devastation.

The storm had washed straight down and across the field. There was a slight gradient and the gulleys were over a foot deep and one hundred yards long. Seeds, plants and fertilisers were washed into the road. The silt was two feet deep in places.

More sowing had to be abandoned for a week before the soil had dried out sufficiently.

Plant pulling was just about to commence. Customers were screaming for their orders. In desperation, I motored to Lincolnshire and back in one day. I had seen an advert for sprout plants. I went to see the health of the plants. I wanted to meet the man. We made a deal straight away. I would buy, and trade on, two hundred and fifty thousand sprout plants the following week.

Little did I know the weather would turn very hot and humid. When the plants arrived early one morning at seven o'clock and we were ready to unload them into our rented cold store, they were already steaming and yellow. Many thousands were completely useless. My customers were very disappointed. The plants were not up to my usual standard.

A sale of some good farming land in the South Petherton district was scheduled for June 30th 1986. I had a conversation with my bank manager. He gave a very cautious approval to my proposition. I had a limit above which I must not go. We bought thirteen acres only. We had wanted to buy eighty five acres.

July saw a big improvement in the weather. Hot and dry, ideal for sowing the last varieties of March/May cauliflower, late winter savoy and January King. The orders for plants kept coming by post and telephone. Five million leek plants were required from Holland. They would be ready at the rate of one million plants per week from the middle of July.

Then there came that fateful day – July 13th 1986.

Little did I realise how close to death I was. I hadn't kept my bookwork up to scratch. My cash flow position with my bank was in a parlous state. But, I didn't die, I have survived, with great difficulty at times but I am still here.

8

SELF IMPOSED THERAPY – TAKING OVER

During January 1988 my therapy became even more difficult. It had to be self-imposed. No longer was I sheltered from the harsh realities of life. My occupational therapist, Jenny, was not available to lead me into new interests. Alison, my physiotherapist was no longer giving me regular exercises. Roger, the occupational therapist in the heavy workshop was not there to give advice and help when I was trying to make rocking horses.

I got up each morning but there seemed nothing to do. I could drive to the village to collect my newspaper but my world seemed empty, without purpose. It was most distressing. I often cried, not for long but the tears seemed to let out the feelings of frustration that were pent up within me.

I bought a lot of new workshop equipment including an electric bandsaw, a workshop bench, electric drills and planer, a hand saw and set squares. I bought a second-hand woodwork bench and was fully equipped to begin making rocking horses.

When I got down to work I found many problems. I had to work on my own. Standing was very tiring and there was no one to talk to. I had an armchair to sit in but it gave me little comfort. My right leg stuck out when I sat down. My right knee and right ankle seemed to be permanently locked. This put great strain upon the hip joint. Only by being in a vertical position or by lying down, did I have any respite from the dull aching pain in my right hip.

Walking gave some relief but I had a distinct limp which was very tiring. I often walked a mile in the morning, but I had to have a complete rest afterwards. The early months of 1988 were very difficult.

Spring 1988 and I wanted to do something active in connection with farming. Potatoes have been a most important crop in South Somerset farming circles since they were introduced into this country from South America by Sir Walter Raleigh in the late 16th century. I thought I could do a research project as part of my therapy. For three or four months I daily talked to elderly farm workers about growing potatoes in the early part of this century. Which varieties were grown then? How were they planted and harvested? What was the yield? When did tractors take over from horses? All the information has been fully recorded and will be used in future. It was a very worthwhile exercise as it brought me into contact with so many people. It kept me sane. I have always been an extrovert and I just wanted to be the same character I always was.

Peggy and I were still living at Rydon Farm. It is a fine hamstone house set in a truly rural environment. It has a large flower, fruit and vegetable garden. I had been born there and lived there until I was six years old. We had come back in 1957.

Peggy had to approach me very gently about leaving Rydon Farm, I couldn't face that decision. I only wanted to get better. I thought that one day I should drive a tractor again. But in my heart of hearts I knew that was an impossibility.

In May 1988, Peggy and I had a serious talk about

what we should do. The property market seemed very buoyant at the time. I was nearly sixty years old and Peggy had had a very difficult two years. We decided to sell Rydon Farmhouse. We had obtained planning permission to replace the burnt out buildings with a four-bedroomed house. To make the package even more attractive, we would sell five acres of adjoining land.

It didn't make the reserve which we wanted when we tried to sell it at auction. But within two weeks we sold the house and one acre. A further four weeks and we had sold the derelect buildings and four acres. People often say to me 'Don't you miss Rydon?' 'Not a bit' I reply, 'I haven't been so happy for years'.

Whilst leaving Rydon Farm had its regrets, we were able to say goodbye in style. My sixtieth birthday was on Friday 30th June 1988 and on the Saturday we had a special celebration. We had a marquee on the front lawn and a reception area in the front garden shed. There were sixty-five guests present (ten more had been unable to attend). To each lady I gave a corsage of orchids. To each man, all of whom had worn evening dress. I gave a carnation as a buttonhole.

Drinks and food were provided by outside caterers and the evening finished with a singsong accompanied by a friend on an electric organ. It may seem unimportant to my recovery but I feel it was my way of saying 'Thank You' to a marvellous group of relations and friends who had supported Peggy and myself through a bad patch on our march through life.

But there was another side to all the frivolity and laughter.

9

MORE OF THE SAME MEDICINE

During July 1988, I was shown a photograph of myself and Peggy taken at my birthday party. Whilst I looked quite smart and Peggy was at her radiant best, I was somewhat uneasy when I came to carry out a closer inspection of myself. I was standing but my general deportment was not right. I knew my right hand was very weak and when walking, I had a very distinct limp. The photograph showed my right shoulder drooping badly.

I felt very dejected. I had reached a plateau on the long road to recovery, but I was beginning to wonder if I would ever find a way forward despite all the hard work that I had already put into the job. I was not satisfied with my progress.

'Could do better' was often featured in my school reports and I felt I must do better. Whilst I had reached a plateau, I felt trapped there. If I really wanted to make progress, I had to find out what the faults were and how they could be put right.

In August 1988, I decided I must return to professional physiotherapy treatment. I contacted a physiotherapist who lives locally. Di used to work in the National Health Service and now practises privately. She has since been joined there by Judith. They are both members of the Chartered Society of Physiotherapists. I went to have a session every Tuesday morning for a year to get the posture right.

What was wrong and how could it be put right? Put very simply: a lot was wrong with my stance and it could be put right only by concentration on the faults and some bloody hard work!

If we may concentrate on what was wrong first. Starting with my trunk and pelvis. It was very stiff. I walked very stiff-legged. The same remarks applied to the right knee and right ankle. When sitting on a dining-room chair, my right leg stuck out stiffly in front of me. My right hip and right knee were not bent naturally. The same remarks applied to my right ankle. There was some swelling behind the knee and in front of the ankle.

The upper right trunk, under the right arm and across the right shoulder were extremely weak. There was no muscle working properly in that area. Since there were no active muscles there, there was no firm support for my head. This made my head fall away and I literally, drooped.

The extremities of the body are the most difficult to correct. The right big toe stuck up constantly and there seemed to be no muscles to pull it down.

The most complicated pieces of human machinery are the arm, the wrist, the hand and the fingers. The spasticity in this area has always been very deep and will require a long time to correct. This is likely to continue for some time and I shall always have difficulty with a certain task, the only one I really cannot do, buttoning up the left-hand shirt-sleeve.

As well as the weaknesses described in my stature, there has also been some difficulty with my vision. The small muscles which held my right eye in place within its own socket have been damaged. When I was in hospital the eye specialist told me that my right eye would be

93

permanently damaged and that vision would be seriously impaired. The centre of my vision is blurred and hazy, the peripheral vision is normal. However, with continual use it appears that the centre of the eye is slowly clearing and because I am able to move my head more and more to the right I am able to see that much better all the time. For a very long time, I appeared, as I have said, starey eyed. My right eye did not move at the same speed as my left eye. There was little which could be done for my eyes, only time could end this fault.

The stroke had taken away the power of speech initially. This may sound very bland and uninteresting but it was completely devastating. I had always been a 'communicator' having learnt to recite for my grandparents when a very small boy. My early efforts to improve my diction seemed to be lost forever.

It required a super-human effort to overcome this deficiency. I could hear most words spoken to me but making any comment, however small, seemed to be impossible. The frustration seemed to be complete. I was very distressed. I cried loud and long on many occasions.

When the stroke occurred, the lack of blood to the vocal chords meant that I could not speak, though I could understand what was being said to me. There are thousands of brain cells not used in the normal person. I have had to learn to harness these and speak from another part of the brain. This frustration was very intense and lasted for some time.

I couldn't speak any words for more than two weeks. When asked how I felt, I could only mumble unrecognisable sounds. Sometimes I would nod my head in agreement or shake my head if I did not agree with what was said to me.

When I came back to South Petherton Hospital, twelve days after the stroke, I was still not speaking normally.

I remember being put in a wheelchair and being alone in the ambulance for the ten mile journey. I had lost a considerable amount of weight, not less than two stones. I was very confused. During the journey I thought why couldn't I go home? The business needed me badly. There was so much to do but I couldn't do it. I cried softly to myself. But when we got to South Petherton and I was welcomed by the staff, many of whom I had known all my life I felt relief. Perhaps I *had* to learn to speak again.

It is difficult to remember the first words I spoke. Probably, 'hello darling' to Peggy. I wanted to say, 'I love you' but I couldn't do it at first. These words contained too much emotion. But gradually, I overcame this disability.

The right-hand side of my mouth seemed very swollen, though I now know the muscles on the right hand side of my face were affected. My tongue and mouth seemed very swollen. It was like going to the dentist, having an injection and for two or three hours it can be difficult to speak normally.

Imagine for a few moments if you would, what it is like to see everything, hear everything, know everything that is going on around you, and your mouth is swollen, as at the dentist not for an hour, nor for five hours, not for a day, but for weeks on end, maybe for a lifetime.

Sometimes I felt very depressed because I was cut off from other people's conversations. I remember my grandmother Vaux, who had a cataract in one eye and was stone deaf, said that the deafness was much worse than the blindness. I felt the same. Cut off without hope.

Instead of professional speech therapy I have had a marvellous lot of relations and friends who have given me much encouragement through laughter and conversation, stimulation through visual means and through playing scrabble.

People say to me now what was it like not being able to speak.

Just one word, HELL.

Gradually I could say, 'yes' or 'no', 'how are you', 'nice day'. It was single words at first, then short expressions. As I mentioned much earlier, there was a bad incident one night when, unconsciously, I rolled over on my unfeeling right arm.

That night I was very distressed but I was able to speak, through my tears, to my nurse, Janet. From what seemed the blackest of hours, I learned to speak, to put more than two words into a sentence which could be understood by other people.

During this period of several hours when I was at my lowest ebb, I unfolded all my deepest fears, my abject misery. But, having bared my soul to one stranger, she gave me new hope and a new spirit. In the morning, I was very dispirited but I was resolved to speak as normally as I used to.

I know I stumbled repeatedly over the simplest of words. 'Stumble' is a word in common use. I couldn't say 'stumble' for at least six months.

Because of the swelling, when eating my food, I could only chew on the left hand side of my mouth. I had to learn speech therapy exercises from other people. There are many small things which I learnt to do.

My tongue was put out and in repeatedly.

The tongue was moved up and down.

Both exercises were done together.

The tongue was rolled round inside the mouth, The lips had to have exercises.

The mouth was opened and closed repeatedly because the jaw seemed to be tightening up all the time.

The lower jaw had to be exercised by appearing to yawn repeatedly.

After eight years, I look back and think, 'the flames of hell nearly consumed me, but the determination to live, the passion to survive was stronger than any flames'.

My physiotherapy has had to be an exercise in confidence. Confidence that I could do what was asked of me and I had to have complete confidence in my physiotherapists. That confidence has to be from a professional with many years of experience. She has always told me the truth. Sometimes she appears to be bullying me but all the time, she has to be sympathetic. The pain has shown in my face I know and the beads of perspiration have told her when to stop for a few moments.

Di and Judith always told me what was the purpose of the exercises they were doing. The stiffness or spasticity within my right pelvis was the first place for improvement.

At first I had to learn to sit up straight. The angles of the right ankle, the right knee and the right hip had to be brought as closely as possible to ninety degrees.

These joints had to be brought into line with the pelvis which has to provide the base from which all joints were in unison. Only in this way could the right shoulder become level with the left shoulder. It appears that none of us are completely level in our stance.

From this correct sitting position, we have moved on to standing up. The tendency has been to put the left foot forward and use the left leg as lever to get the trunk and the upper part of my body into an upright position.

The muscles at the back of my left femur and in my left buttock are very strong and pronounced.

I must correct this by putting the right foot forward and using my right leg as a lever.

How has it all been done? By persistence, patience and perseverance. It has been a long time but the hard slog is very slowly but very surely paying off.

When I had got used to sitting up normally, I had to move my right foot one inch to the left and then to the right. All the time the right heel had to be pressed down first. This was to control the right knee. It had been very unstable and lacked control.

Having progressed by putting my right heel down flat repeatedly, I had to put more weight on the ball of my foot. This meant walking with both knees slightly bent. This is an elementary exercise to a normal person. To the stroke patient, it is a movement that has to be learnt from the very beginning.

The next exercise was kneeling down on all fours. In this way the right hand and the right arm was stretched and the ninety degree syndrome was obvious.

The hands were at ninety degrees to the wrists.

The wrists at ninety degrees to the arms.

The arms to the trunk.

The trunk to the femurs.

The femurs to the knees.

The knees to the ankles.

Perfectly elementary to the normal person.

From this position of kneeling, I progressed to balancing. By taking an increased weight on my hands and arms, I was able to lift my right knee off the floor. Then I changed to lifting the left knee.

I collapsed in a heap on the floor several times. It was a stressful exercise at first but having got this far without actually breaking any bones, I was determined to go on. And on. And on.

After many sessions of these exercises, we moved to strengthening the muscles of the right shoulder.

When kneeling down on all fours, pressure was put on the right shoulder. This was done more by 'thumping', not a continuous pressure. The muscles had to be stimulated, to waken them from their deep slumber.

The last limb requiring detailed attention was the right arm. It had originally hung limp and lifeless by my side.

If completely ignored by the patient or any helpers, the limb withers; not away but becomes curled up and in some cases, the hand is in a permanent position across the chest and in extreme cases, close to the chin.

I was determined to avoid, at all costs, such disfigurement.

In the autumn of 1989, I started electrical therapy. Four suction pads, about one inch in diameter, were attached to the right lower arm and wrist. A very minor electrical shock was then fed into the pads for ten minutes.

Painful, yes. But I had got used to pain and discomfort. I had to endure any pain to achieve the thrill of fuller recovery.

This treatment was repeated three times in half an hour. It loosened the tightness in my wrist and hand.

There had been little or no feeling within my forearm. The small muscles between the skin and the bone had not been working for three and a half years.

Now we come to the right hand. The stroke appears to have destroyed completely that part of the brain which sends messages to the hand. But the brain has thousands of unused cells. They have to be brought back into use.

Within the wrist, the hand and the fingers are countless movements. Turn the wrist over and back again. Open the hand and close it again. Extend the arm to shake hands.

There are hundreds of intricate movements which have to be learnt, all the time remembering that the part of the brain responsible for these movements may or may not have been destroyed.

Lastly, the electrical shock treatment has been on the wrist and fingers. The right thumb is seventy-five per cent normal. I must take care at all times not to allow the thumb to be curled into the palm of the hand.

The right index finger is sixty-five per cent normal and the little finger is sixty per cent normal.

The middle two fingers are more difficult for some reason.

The electrical therapy introduces a shock to the outside of the fingers and small sensations follow with the fingers.

I have found it very difficult to describe. But there is improvement.

One doctor said at the time of the stroke 'the blood cells within the brain are like the railway lines at Clapham Junction Station but multiplied many times over. Some of the main lines are completely destroyed or permanently damaged but there are many secondary routes. Only perseverence and patience can encourage the secondary routes to take over from the main line routes'.

My speech is normal. In fact, I have a habit of 'rabbiting on' – quite normal many friends say! I feel so lucky to be able to do so much. I want to talk about it and encourage other stroke patients that the long hard slog can give a new dimension to life.

10

HOLIDAYS BEFORE AND AFTER THE STROKE

While 1988 was a year in which many momentous decisions had been made, some of them sad and, at the time, very traumatic, there was another aspect of my life that was enjoyable and relaxing. Peggy had worked without rest for two years to nurse me back to my improved state of health. She and Philip had kept the farm going and she had continued with the bed and breakfast guests.

But she needed a holiday badly. Could I manage to accompany her for a three week holiday? Or would I have to stay with friends? Nothing daunted, I chose a holiday. Where should we go? We thought of staying in the United Kingdom but this didn't appeal to my adventurous spirit. Then we thought about the many holidays we had had abroad.

In 1962, we had a motoring holiday across France and Belgium to Holland and Denmark. There we saw the land of Danish bacon, Carlsberg lager, the house of Hans Christian Andersen and the Little Mermaid in Copenhagen Harbour. However, driving across Europe would be very difficult for Peggy so that idea was abandoned.

What about the holidays we had had in Italy? We had been to Venice and Florence for a cultural tour in 1964. However, walking among the galleries and beside the canals in Venice was rejected – I couldn't walk that far.

Whilst it would have been possible to see art in many guises in either city, I felt I couldn't really relax.

The same applied to Sorrento and the Amalfi coast. There had been so much to see in Rome but I didn't feel I was ready to listen to an official guide for two or three hours telling us all about the capital's ancient Roman history.

What about Spain and Portugal? We had had holidays on the Algarve coast and Madeira. They had been two week holidays only. We wanted a longer vacation. What about another cruise?

In 1984, we had taken a cruise from Italy through the Suez Canal to Southern Jordan, back across the Red Sea to Egypt and ended up in Athens. Could I undertake such a trip? We had flown to Naples and cruised through the Straits of Messina by moonlight. Very romantic! It had been planned to stay one day at Rhodes but the sea was very rough and we sailed slowly round the coast of the Island before leaving to reach Port Said and the Canal during daylight hours.

We left Port Said about 11.45 p.m. at the head of a convoy of twenty five great ships of many nations carrying a wide variety of cargoes. A recording of the Royal Marines Band playing *Land of Hope and Glory* and many other patriotic songs had awakened my love of my home and my England and it brought a lump to my throat and a tear to my eye. We then sailed to Akaba in Southern Jordan.

We disembarked and 500 passengers and 30 staff were taken by bus across the desert, close to the Rose Red lost city of Petra. Try as I might the next event would have been a complete impossibility now. It had been a never-to-be forgotten sight – five hundred passengers on *horseback* being led through the desert to the great city lost for hundreds of years to human eyesight.

We returned by road to Akaba and sailed across the Red Sea to Qadzir. There we disembarked at Safaga at 4.30 in the morning and went by coach overland to Luxor on the River Nile. Midday in the middle of the Egyptian desert was really hot when the temperature rose above 105° F. In the afternoon, we crossed the Nile and went back thousands of years in history when we visited the Valley of the Ancient Kings of Egypt.

We sailed overnight to Suez and next morning left to visit Cairo, the Pyramids and the Sphinx. We returned across the desert to Port Said and set sail for Israel. The first day there, I went to Nazareth and the Sea of Galilee but I didn't feel very well. Next day I had to stay on board ship. Something to do with the water in Cairo. Never drink water or tea or have an ice cube! I had had a whisky and ice – seems harmless – it wasn't!

Peggy went to Jerusalem, Jericho and the Dead Sea. I had to stay on board ship and didn't move very far from my cabin throughout the day.

Our cruise finished in Athens which we found rather disappointing as it is being ruined by all the air pollution. From Athens we flew home to Heathrow.

It had been a holiday to remember. Physically somewhat exhausting but quite different from any other we had before. We had met many English-speaking people and families from other nations. Their conversation had always been stimulating.

The big question was, could I do it again? Peggy had thoroughly enjoyed the first cruise. I didn't want to be a burden to her. We thought and talked about it for several days. Finally we decided that, in spite of the cost, we could do it.

Then the planning started. I must pay tribute to the staff of our travel agents, R.E. Bath Limited, Their help and advice were invaluable and the whole trip went very smoothly.

We decided to fly to the Far East and cruise through part of the South China Sea and Pacific Ocean. To begin with, what were the facilities for the disabled? A wheelchair was essential when moving about the various airports of the world. They were available at every airport. In fact, when I embarked or disembarked from any plane, the wheelchair with an attendant, was waiting for me. A wheelchair at the airports was the only facility for my disablement which I needed. Everywhere else I walked as best I could.

We planned to leave Heathrow on November 1st 1988. This part of any holiday is now always the worst for me. I can't lift and carry cases to the car. So I've learnt to do other things away from the house during case-packing time. We were collected by a good friend, John and his wife Pam at 8.00 a.m. We were due to leave Heathrow at 1.00 p.m. A wheelchair was available and after passports, tickets, luggage labels were checked, we had time to relax before we started the long journey to Hong Kong.

We had an hour's flight to Paris where we were due to meet various flights from other European cities and from America. We were going to set off at 5.00 p.m. Then there was a delay. No one told us when we might expect to take off or anything like that. So we had another cup of coffee. There were further delays.

Fortunately I have been a fairly placid man all my life and since that fateful day in 1986 I have learned to cope with many disappointments and frustrations. By 8.00 p.m., many of the passengers were getting very angry. It was most frustrating until we were all given a 'light continental snack' of second-class ham sandwiches made with one-day-old stale bread! And there was another cup of coffee! Eventually and with tempers rising by the minute, we were allowed to board at 11.00 p.m.

There were several disabled people in the party who, as is the case with all plane journeys, get on board first. Peg and I were given a very comfortable seat with plenty of leg room.

The evening meal was served at 1.00 a.m. Once on board, I felt very tired and quickly settled down to sleep. I realised that due to flying east, there would not be many hours of total darkness. The plane made a refuelling stop at Bombay. It was midday local time. I had a stroll through the airport lounges to ease my right leg.

Our next stop was to be Bangkok where we arrived at 6.00 p.m. local time. As the plane was behind the scheduled time, no passengers were allowed to depart from the plane whilst cleaning and revictualling took place.

We eventually reached Hong Kong at about 11.00 p.m. which was just before the airport closes strictly at midnight. I was somewhat tired but not overtired. It is a most spectacular sight to see Hong Kong lit up, from the sky at night. The plane landed from the direction of the sea and flew towards the city. As it landed I realised that we were travelling amongst the traffic on the roads and all that time we were moving at a hundred miles an hour towards the skyscrapers! Quite a hairy experience.

On landing, a wheelchair, which had been previously ordered when we booked the flight in the UK, was provided, as I stepped off the plane. An airport steward whisked us away from the normal route taken by passengers and Peggy and I went straight through customs very quickly.

P & O provided couriers to take care of the luggage and cope with many enquiries which were made by various passengers at the airport. The congestion around the airport as all the passengers were trying to leave, was very considerable and somewhat confusing. I had been travelling from Paris nearly 24 hours and was very pleased to reach the Hotel Verala at approximately 11.45 local time. Wednesday November 3rd seems to have been a missing day!

Peggy was merely carrying some light luggage and we were very frustrated at the hotel that night as we found that we had no cases. We thought they had been stolen. Eventually I got to bed at 2.30 a.m. and was soon asleep, helped by a sleeping tablet. We had no night clothes and nothing with which to clean our teeth. We were very tired, very worried and more than a little frustrated. Peggy and I had visions of having lost all our luggage. It evoked memories of the disappointment we had in South Africa many years previously when Peggy had had her jewel box stolen.

Fortunately our luggage arrived in the morning and we spent much of the early part of the day reading local history and trying to become acclimatised to the hot atmosphere. Our bedroom was on the twenty-second floor and overlooked a park which was right in the middle of the business centre of the city. Men, and a few women, were out jogging or doing physical exercises from early in the morning till late at night. Land for recreation is at such a prohibitive price, people seem to take exercise when and where they can.

In the afternoon, I decided that I might try to board a funicular railway. The train started just two hundred yards from the back of the hotel. I could walk that far in spite of the number of pedestrians on the raised pavements. The railway didn't seem to be a bar to my walking. As we ascended to thirteen hundred feet, we had a panoramic view of the city and harbour. The view was somewhat spoilt as the heavy drizzle quickly turned to a tropical thunderstorm. We had a cup of tea at the restaurant at the top and descended the same way. For me, another mountain had been climbed successfully.

In the early evening, there was an organised outing around the harbour, a visit to the Aberdeen Market and an evening meal aboard one of the floating Chinese restaurants. I had flown 10,000 miles and gone up and down in the funicular railway so why couldn't I go on board a little ship around the harbour?

We (I mean Peggy and the other guests) were picked up from the hotel about 6.30 p.m. The one mile journey to the embarkation point took twenty minutes, as there is such traffic and congestion on the roads in Hong Kong.

I had been told that I must see Hong Kong at night from the harbour. And it's true. The lights from the skyscrapers; the chugging of the hundreds of small boats; the constant noise from the vast number of new buildings under construction which seemed to be built day and night; the constant passage of the ferries crisscrossing the water; the high rise blocks of flats with families crammed in 200 square feet per family; these are the lasting memories of what for me was an unforgettable experience.

When we toured the Aberdeen Fish Market we saw hundreds of traditional Chinese fishing boats. Not only were they used for fishing sometimes in deep sea waters many miles from Hong Kong but they carried the wives of the crew and their families. It was interesting to hear that ten per cent of each catch has to be sold to China. Many of the children never go to school. The fish market is a hot bed of piracy and underground offences. The squalor on these boats had to be seen to be believed.

When our boat got to the floating restaurant I was helped aboard and treated with the utmost courtesy. There were hundreds of people in the six restaurants. Guests were expected to eat the traditional Chinese food with chopsticks. For me, that was quite impossible. So I

107

asked for a knife and fork instead. The meal consisted of nine courses. I'd never eaten Chinese food before but I found it most enjoyable. The custom seems to spurn alcoholic drink but weak Chinese tea was available at all times. That night I slept soundly. Another milestone had been reached, I had eaten out on the threshold of China.

The next morning I felt I could tackle any journey. Why not a ride on a hydrofoil to the mainland? To Macao, the last outpost of the Portuguese Empire. The crossing took one and half hours. It gave me time to reflect that here I was, disabled, a stroke victim, walking, with difficulty, with a stick, amongst hundreds of passengers who were mostly Chinese aboard a hydrofoil. And it didn't seem to matter to them. When we got to Macao, I realised why it didn't matter to them.

Chinese people love gambling. They will gamble all day. Macao is a 'free city' so there seem to be no regulations of any kind. A tour was laid on and it was the only part of the trip to the Far East when I felt slightly nervous. There seemed to be pickpockets and merchants of tourist goods who had less than an honest intent.

I did have a most enjoyable lunch in one of the hotels. In the afternoon, which was very hot, I saw why Macao is the most densely populated place in the world. I saw blocks of flats, hundreds of them where families live, mother and father and maybe six or more children in less than two hundred square feet. And there is nowhere to have a garden, nowhere except outside the windows to hang your clothes, nowhere to go for exercise. Nothing to do. Except scrape a living in the casinos. Begging is very much a part of life in Macao, especially amongst children.

On November 6th, the cruise proper started. Cases packed and ready for collection by 11.00 a.m., I had time to relax and talk to other people in the hotel lounge.

Disabled people everywhere seem to have a common bond and I talked with a lady from South Illinois in the United States. She had arthritis rather badly and could only walk short distances with difficulty. You meet so many people from so many countries. That's what I like about cruising. Conversation never seems to flag. What's the climate like? What do you think about the American President?

I am a very inquisitive sort of person who likes to know what a community thinks. Would the United States go to war again? I've learned that if you don't ask the questions you don't know the answers. My early training by my father in the art of public speaking had not deserted me. In fact, since my stroke I have learned to see and perceive more than I did before.

We were all taken by coaches to our embarkation point at a deep water jetty in the harbour. Once on board at about 4.30 p.m., I had time and energy to go on deck to watch the final preparations and victualling before the boat sailed at 6.30 p.m. Then I could have a rest before the Captain's cocktail reception.

This was a most grand affair. Ladies wore their finery with many dripping diamonds showing from earrings, brooches and pendants. Likewise most of the men wore evening dress. I had a tuxedo with a buttonhole and Peggy wore her finest evening dress. I felt we both looked the part of tourists.

As I find I cannot cope with a lot of noise, I had earlier asked for a table in the dining room with only four or six persons. Cross talk across a table with twelve or more people, I find very tiring. Our companion at our meals turned out to be first class. A retired army officer, David, had recently lost his wife with cancer. Increasing blindness had persuaded him to go cruising before it was too late to see the many attractions of the world. He was full of stories from the past. How he met, when he was seven, Alice of 'Alice in Wonderland'. She was a very old lady in 1917. The head waiter, who was Italian, noticed I had difficulty cutting up my food. He immediately came to my rescue and was always on hand at every evening meal to give any assistance I required. I used to find it rather distressing, and even slightly humiliating to have my food cut up at any meal. But people are genuinely very helpful. Perhaps they think 'tomorrow it may be me'.

Next morning, I was awake fairly early and saw, through our cabin porthole, a ship sailing very slowly up a river. I got dressed straightaway and was on deck to see the slow manoeuvres as the boat turned round in a comparatively confined space. The port which serves Guang Chou, or Canton to the older generations, was a bustling affair. There were containers everywhere as the port serves as an export/import centre for the vast hinterland of Southern China.

After breakfast, there was a delay of about an hour due to official passport controls. When our party of 500 people was ready to disembark, we were greeted by a group of children of about five to ten years old. They were dressed in uniforms similar to those seen in 'toytown'. Their playing on tin whistles, drums etc. left very much to be desired! And that's being very kind! But the thought was there – foreign visitors must be welcomed to China in their traditional manner.

During our short tour of Canton there was much of interest to me. Our official guide spoke immaculate English. In the fields alongside the roads leading to the city there appeared to be no tractors. But there were thousands and thousands of people everywhere. There were hundreds of lorries but few cars. And there were bicycles everywhere.

After a lunch that was more like a banquet, I had an

unforgettable encounter. The Chinese are very proud of their children. Education may start when children are only two and a half years old. All men and women have a job, so the state takes care of any children. On our sightseeing tour we were taken to a school where many of the children were as young as two and a half years old and up to ten years old. We got out of the bus and crossed the road to see the children in their classroom and in their play area. One of the teachers spoke quite good English. She explained the system and answered many questions.

I was standing around looking at the children playing and singing as children anywhere do. Some of the older children had learned some nursery rhymes which they recited to us in English. All of a sudden, I felt a little hand in mine. Even Peggy was rarely allowed to hold my right hand. It was so sensitive. But here was a little Chinese boy, no more than six or seven years old who wanted to hold my hand. To him, I wasn't disabled. I just walked with a stick. He greeted me in halting English, 'How are you, sir, welcome to China'. In an instant, I almost burst into tears. But that's what cruising is all about. People meeting people from different countries with different religions and different races and ethnic groups meeting people from another country, thousands of miles away. Politicians may posture and fight but people are friendly and warm-hearted.

This very small and seemingly insignificant Chinese boy taught me a lot about myself and my condition. Previously, I had felt diffident about myself. I felt I had to apologise all the time because I couldn't do the things that an able-bodied person can do. But that little Chinese boy accepted me as I was, warts and all. This was a most important step on my road to recovery. Psychologically another barrier had been breached.

After the visit to China we set sail for the capital of the Philippine Islands, Manila. On the first morning at sea, the captain made an important announcement over the tannoy system. 'There's a hurricane ahead with its centre close to the Philippines and, in the interests of passenger safety, I am afraid I must cancel the visit to Manila'.

The next two or three days were pretty difficult ones for me. The ship was sailing about 200 miles south of the centre of the storm. Although there was only a little rain in our area, the sea itself was very disturbed with many 'white horses' on the waves. Because I was probably 100 feet above the sea level, I could not accurately gauge the amount of rise and fall but it felt sometimes as if it was as much as forty feet. This made walking about very difficult for me. Fortunately, I have never suffered from sea sickness. I moved about with the utmost caution. I was never far from handrails when on deck. When there were no handrails, I always walked close to the walls on my left hand side. It was very difficult but I survived without falling over. Another milestone had been passed on my path to recovery. Or more particularly, a small step along the long road that leads to complete recovery.

Our next port of call was Kota Kinabalu, capital of Sabah, the most easterly and largest of the Malay states. When we arrived there, I realised the ship didn't go to a quayside. It weighed anchor in deep water about a half a mile offshore in a sheltered harbour. It was very hot that day with the temperature well over 90°F and the air was very humid. I felt I wanted to stay on board. Other people with heart problems declined to go ashore as well. Peggy, however, joined the party that went ashore for four or five hours. I spent the time thinking about the holiday so far. Making notes for further reference. Soaking up the warm atmosphere, although not sunbathing. It was too hot for that.

We left Kota Kinabalu in the early evening and had two further days cruising to our next destination – Thailand. We sailed into Sattahip early one morning and disembarked after breakfast. The two hour drive through the Thai countryside was very interesting for me. Farmers everywhere take more than a casual look at farming in other countries.

I always sat in the front seat when I was on any coach trip. It was more convenient for my right leg. In consequence, I had a good view and could ask our guide many questions. I had heard about manioc growing in the United Kingdom. 'What was it like?' To European eyes, small parsnips. 'How deep does it grow?' Nearly two feet. 'Who worked the land?' Men and women and children. 'Was there any machinery?' Only a very small amount. 'Were any tractors used?' Just a few. What was the yield of manioc per acre in a good season?' This question floored the guide. 'Did Thailand have an ideal climate for manioc?' Yes, more or less a completely monsoon type of climate. 'What type of soil is ideal for manioc growing?' Deep sandy soil. 'What was the total value of the crop to the Thai economy?' Here again the question was rather baffling to the guide.

Disabled I may be in walking but my ability to ask searching questions seems to be unabated.

The coach had a toilet on board. Every coach had an attendant, who spoke no English, as well as an official English-speaking guide. I went to the toilet and was very surprised when the attendant accompanied me to the door. Although I could walk quite easily, the guide thought I might need help at some point. In Thailand that's the normal attitude to the disabled. Help was at hand with every turn whether getting down from a bus, walking up steps – everywhere, I was never far from help.

When we got to Bangkok at about midday, we found our bedrooms were not ready for us. We had to wait about half an hour in the hotel lobby. Eventually we had our lunch in a most palatial dining room. After lunch, our bedroom on the 27th floor was ready for occupation. It was sumptuous. There was a king-sized double bed. Orchids by the bed, exotic chocolates to eat and a magnificent view from the windows. What more could any man ask for?

After a rest on the bed, I was ready for the afternoon's adventures. It was very hot when we boarded the bus to go on the sightseeing tour. The highlight was the visit to the King's Palace. I thought I had seen congestion and poverty. When we got off the bus outside the palace, I was surrounded, literally, by men and women, boys and girls of all ages trying to sell anything from postcards to pictures, novelties to nougat. The noise of many raised voices, jostling by the crowd, people begging for money – all these things I found somewhat trying. But there were helpful hands available. Without them I doubt whether I could have crossed the busy road. Despite traffic lights, cars seem to pay little heed to my disability.

Once across the road, I was glad to get into the comparative calm of the King's Palace grounds. The next hour I saw sights of indescribable beauty and splendour. If I may, I would like to set the scene.

A cloudless afternoon with the sun pouring down on many hundreds of tourists. The constant 'click' of cameras. A steady stream of Buddhist monks wandering to and fro. And the centre piece, or rather centre pieces – the temples of the King's Palace. Many of them had eighty-foot spires which were encrusted with one-inch square wafers of gold leaf stuck on the outside of the towers. All this work had been done by hand. Over the centuries, it had been a 'labour of love' by the monks.

114

The most spectacular sights were the golden and emerald buddhas. In the centre of the Palace grounds is a small temple. You could enter only if you removed any footwear. I couldn't do this. Peggy told me that once inside, you were required to sit on the floor. There were no chairs or tables. In the inner sanctum in a dimly lit room from any sunlight, sat the Emerald Buddha.

At the top of an altar the Buddha sat cross-legged. It was about three feet high. In the centre of another temple she saw a solid gold Buddha. In earlier centuries, marauding hoards had tried to steel this great treasure. But the King's courtiers at the time had hidden the Buddha under a plaster cast. When it was moved years later, it was dropped and broken, revealing the Buddha. It also weighs three tons. Three tons of solid gold!! A priceless treasure if there ever was one. The two hours spent wandering about in the King's Palace grounds were very hot, slightly tiring but unforgettable.

I was very glad when the coaches arrived to take us back to the hotel. It was a Sunday about five o'clock. To go to the horse racing on Sunday afternoons is the main pastime in Bangkok. Our coach took us on a tour of the city, but the last two miles of which were close to the race track. Traffic in Bangkok is always chaotic. That Sunday it took over an hour to do two miles. Bicycles and cars were everywhere. And the 'tutt-tutts'! They are like three wheeled taxis. A man sits on the saddle with two passengers seated behind him. There is a two-stroke engine and there are pedals. The 'tutt-tutts' weaved in and out of traffic everywhere. The noise is incredible. The air pollution is awful. Again these were sights and sounds that were completely unforgettable.

After a rest at our hotel, I was ready for the next outing. We went to a posh Thai restaurant. It was a long walk through a crowded shopping precinct. When I got there,

I found I had to climb steep stairs as the restaurant was on the second floor. Then, all visitors were required to remove any footwear. I had to do it or I couldn't have entered. Once inside, the restaurant was very dimly lit. Its tables seemed to be rather close to the floor. Thai people squat down to eat at their tables. Visitors are required to sit on very low benches with their legs dangling beneath the table and close to the floor. Waiters (there seemed to be no waitresses) kneeled beside you to take your order and serve the meal.

The meal itself had many interesting features. A bowl of plain brown rice is available to clear your palate between courses. It is the custom to eat only from one dish at a time. There were eight to ten dishes of food, mostly vegetables. What was in the meat dishes I do not know. And I didn't ask!! I just enjoyed the meal.

After the meal, we were entertained by traditional Thai dancers. There were twelve women but only two men. The men always wore face masks and never danced with any of the women. The girls were fabulous. One look at their hands and fingers and your could see that they had never done any work. Their finger nails were probably three or four inches long, maybe longer. It was particularly noticeable that the girls' feet seemed to be rather flat and larger than western feet. Perhaps because it is a custom that women never wear shoes, their feet become larger and wider. The dances had many intricate patterns. The music was always slow to western ears and the movements were somewhat sensuous to my mind. It was a grand evening and I was ready for my king-sized bed by ten o'clock.

Next morning, our destination was the floating market of Bangkok. After an hour's journey through crowded streets, along bumpy roads, we arrived at a landing stage. Here was a real challenge. I wanted to go by boat to the

116

market. However the boat was only wide enough for two people and long enough for twelve passengers. Because it is always very hot and, in the monsoon season, it rains a lot, the boat has a canopy about four feet high. But, how was I to get into the boat? That's where the Thai tradition scored heavily. Three men saw my difficulties and immediately lifted me under the canopy and into the seat. Easy, wasn't it?

The flat-bottomed boats are called *Klongs*. They are powered by two-stroke engines. The engine is mounted on the rudder which is hinged to the boat. All the canals and waterways have perhaps four or five feet of water in them. When going straight ahead, the skipper puts the rudder into the water and revs up the engines. At the corners, the rudder and engine are removed from the water and the boat glides round and starts its next straight run.

When we got to the central market, I had to get out of this narrow, swaying boat which was floating in very murky water. How was I going to do it? Not on my own to be sure. But help was soon available and two strong men lifted me onto dry land. It had been a slightly humiliating experience being lifted into and out of a boat by people in a foreign land. But, I had learned to live with humiliation since the stroke. Live with and overcome that slight feeling of inadequacy.

After another wonderful lunch at the Rose Gardens, I had time to relax and watch the side shows in the gardens. I watched the elephants moving with ease, the trunks of teak wood that were twenty foot long and maybe over a ton in weight. Our visit to Bangkok finished in the afternoon in spectacular style. There was traditional Thai dancing, a Thai wedding, Thai wrestling and Thai sword dancing. In this, two women held twelve feet long bamboo poles and banged them together. Two men then danced

117

within the poles, all the time the banging became faster and louder and the foot movements were more complicated.

We were driven, in a convoy, back to the boat accompanied by police outriders. The traffic is absolutely awful in the evening rush hour and our party had to be back by six o'clock before sailing at seven, for Singapore.

After three days in Singapore I was ready to go home. But, first we had to get to the airport and board the plane. What chaos! The departure time from Singapore was 10 p.m. We were collected from our hotel at about seven. The coach trip only took half an hour. At the airport, the luggage, which was coming in another truck, failed to arrive for over an hour. I had ordered a wheelchair when I left England but there was no wheelchair to be seen. There were only a few seats and I gave up mine to more elderly people. There were thousands and thousands of people and it seemed to be that it was a general holiday in Singapore. Singapore is a staging post for many airlines throughout the Pacific Basin. The customs officials, and especially those on drug enforcement duties, were very officious. To add insult to injury we had to pay one hundred pounds excess luggage charge. At the end of three weeks holiday we didn't want that headache. Three cheers for the plastic money card.

Eventually, and after walking a long way, I got on our aircraft at 9.45 p.m. After dinner, I slept soundly for six hours. We arrived at Heathrow at 6 a.m. local time. We were glad to be home, and the memories will be with us for ever. I had attempted to go on a cruise the other side of the world. I had succeeded. I hadn't fallen over. I hadn't been a nuisance to other people. People generally accepted me as I was. That in itself gave my morale a great boost. The effort had all been worthwhile.

When we arrived back in South Petherton, the weather

itself was vastly different. There was a cold wind and rain for several days with frost and slippery roads. That's the sort of weather I don't like. I feel I could easily slip over. I might break a leg, or my arms. And there was a reaction to the holiday. We went into temporary accommodation whilst the solicitors sorted out certain legalities regarding the bungalow we thought we had bought. The following three months were a great disappointment.

I had never suffered from claustrophobia. However, the flat itself was very small, vastly different from Rydon Farm. The floors were very bumpy and uneven. The ceilings were very low. The beds were only bunk beds, two feet six wide. The windows were very low. All in all not the most conducive atmosphere for my recovery. I often found myself waking at night feeling very confined and very distressed.

Once the legalities were sorted out the builder chaps pressed on with the work and we moved into our present home in early March 1989. Two mornings later we had a great surprise. My nephew, David, was getting married to Sarah Jane in Sydney, Australia. There was an invitation for Peggy and me. Having been on the cruise, could I go to Australia? It didn't take very long for me to make up my mind and decide that I was physically able to make the trip. The expense had to be considered as well but after a few days of deliberation, Peggy and I, together with my sister decided we would go and have a holiday in Australia.

It's a long way there and we decided to break our journey in Thailand. We left England on April 22nd and had two nights in Bangkok. It is very hot at that time of the year (around 95° F) and because of the heat, the crowds and the pollution I knew it would be more than I could bear. I stayed indoors during the day. So whilst the ladies went on their various shopping expeditions I

119

stayed in the cool of the air conditioned hotel and thought about the possibilities of my next book. Would it be a novel or another autobiography? Would it be based on my early life? If a novel, based upon what? Country life. Where? During my lifetime or earlier. These were some of the thoughts going through my mind at the time.

When we got to Sydney I found there were excellent facilities available for me. Official legislation requires any public utility, museum, art gallery and Parliament buildings must all have wheelchairs available. They are also required to have lifts available for the disabled. A very good idea I saw in Australia was at pavements. At any crossing point, the pavement is lowered so that the disabled can have their wheelchair pushed without any difficulty. It also makes it easier for those who are able to walk with difficulty to go across the roads.

In case you think of Australia as all sunshine and Bondi Beach, it can rain cats and dogs in Sydney. I went to the wedding and had a very good time meeting relatives I hadn't seen for many years. At the reception, we had a tropical thunder storm but fortunately I got out of the car under a canopy. Because I go so slowly when walking, I always avoid the heaviest rain. After staying in Sydney for two or three days for various sightseeing tours, we hired a car and set off on a tour of part of New South Wales and Victoria. Peggy and Nina took it in turns to do the driving while I acted as navigator. That's not difficult in Australia as the road signs are very good. The roads are straight but there is a speed limit of fifty miles an hour.

Our first stop was the capital city of Canberra. It's a beautiful city, especially in Autumn. We were told 'Never go to Canberra until after Anzac Day, April 25th'. Canberra is about 1000 feet above sea level, so it is always liable to frost which never occurs until after April 25th.

After the first frost the colour of the many varieties of trees is superb. Australians think a lot about men and women who fought in the two World Wars. Anzac Day is treated like Armistice Day used to be in the United Kingdom. Nobody works at all, except buses and trains, after 9 a.m. They also pay much attention to the disabled. I felt I was always being treated as an equal.

We got back to Sydney after three weeks of touring and living out of suitcases. We had visited farms and got to know relations, some of whom I'd never seen before. What had I learned on this holiday? First and most important of all, disability isn't a bar to travelling. Though I can't walk as fast as any crowd, there are compensations. I had become a critical observer of any scene. Not that I criticise just for the sake of criticising. But I tend to look much deeper than I used to. I don't just see things on the surface but see what lies underneath.

There are always people ready to talk about their lives. They ask questions about my disability. After more than seven years, I have got over any embarrassment and tell them all about my stroke. But, they must ask first. I don't want to bore people with my story.

Australia didn't seem to offer any opportunities for me even if I had been fit and able. It is a country for the young and athletic type. Farming seems to be a very chancy occupation. There are too many acres and too few people living in Australia. But taken together, the cruise from Hong Kong to Singapore and the holiday in OZ, they were a challenge to me. A challenge which I liked and a challenge which was overcome without too much difficulty at all.

11

SPEECH THERAPY AND PRESENT ACHIEVEMENTS

During the autumn of 1987, just after I started driving my car again, I saw an advertisement in my local newspaper. It said helpers were required at the 'Speech-After-Stroke Club' in Yeovil. Since then it has been renamed the 'Phoenix Club'. It is, I feel, a most appropriate name. The stroke patient feels very cast down in their bewildering world. The club helps in a small way to build up confidence so that, as the phoenix rose from the ashes in Greek mythology so members can speak and sing, work and play as normally as possible.

The club meets weekly for three hours on a Monday morning. We have approximately twenty patients who are members and about twelve carers.

Speech therapy is very much a 'Cinderella Department' of health care. It requires much patience and understanding of the very complicated process of communication through speech.

We assemble at eleven and always exchange simple greetings like 'Good Morning. How are you?' A perfectly elementary expression. But it is the real purpose of the club, to keep things simple.

We must get down to the basics of speech. The eyes see things. The ears hear things. The brain reacts. But the necessary messages from the brain to the tongue and lips do not travel correctly.

The helpers must speak clearly and rather slower than normal. Eye contact is particularly important. The eyes see the lips moving. When the dysphasic person starts to reply, the carer must reply with them.

We use many quiz books. People who have had a stroke are not unintelligent. They just need time to answer any questions.

A useful game is describing in very simple terms the actions in a photograph.

'The woman has been shopping.

She has two children.'

Two simple sentences but the use of simple words restores the broken confidence.

For many of the patients, the use of money is a source of great difficulty. Many cannot differentiate between various coins. One penny and two penny pieces appear the same. Likewise the ten pence piece and the twenty pence piece. The squared corners of a fifty pence piece are usually recognisable and a one pound coin is only known because it is thicker than the others.

Because of these difficulties and the fact that people do cheat when handling money from stroke patients, the patients tend to become withdrawn. By being out of circulation they are not cheated.

The sense of camaraderie between stroke patients is very strong. We can all help one another in some small way.

Recently we had a visit at the club from a speech therapist who works for ADA – Action for Dysphasic Adults.

This is a national charity which was formed in 1979. It has its headquarters in London. Its first county branch was formed in Taunton in 1987.

We aim to provide links between dysphasic people

within Somerset. Dysphasic people feel very cut off from the main stream of life. Clubs like ours help in a small way to rebuild the lost confidence that people once had.

Carers and relatives require support for what, for many is a thankless task. Everybody needs some time away from their patient. The community at large can and does quickly forget the dysphasic person. The Speech-after-Stroke and ADA clubs increase the awareness of the needs of dysphasic people generally.

We raise funds for local and national projects and we keep close contact with our headquarters in London. The headquarters group funds research projects at various universities in England and Wales. We work to improve local services for dysphasic people and their carers.

I joined ADA and attend various committee meetings at Taunton which are held on a six-weekly basis. I feel this work could be of great benefit to me and to others. I often feel that the insider sees more of the action and in this way can benefit those who are less well off.

As I look back now, I consider myself very lucky to be in the position I find myself in today. To have continued in my style of farming, would have been a perpetual struggle. My life then had been fast flowing, never still. There can be no more tractor driving. No more humping the pigs into a lorry. No more humping and heaving of bags of fertiliser or plants to the station. These are all things of the past. I must now look to the future and realise what I can do.

So what has inspired me to keep going and stand beside others as a useful member of the community in which I live?

First there is my God and my Church. Without help from on high, I doubt whether I could have survived. It has been a very hard struggle. There have been moments when the pain and suffering seemed to be more than I could bear. But those moments quickly passed and what must have been Cancerian doggedness took over. The same hidden force that kept me going in those dark days when I was in hospital.

And there is the tenacity. The tenacity to survive. It is in all of us. The capacity to hold on to life. Life has been kind to me. This interlude has been cruel but the old saying 'be cruel to be kind' has surely been right.

The community has played a large part in my recovery. At the outset, they wanted me to survive. I have felt that if they wanted me to survive, survive I must.

The kindness and calmness given to me by Peggy, my sons and their wives and my grandchildren have been of immense value to me. Within my wider family there have been several tragic deaths in recent years.

Wigborough Manor at Lower Stratton, South Petherton has been the hub of the family since my grandparents moved there in 1904. It is a true Elizabethan manor with high ceilings on the ground floor. There are ornate Italian plaster moulds upon the sitting room ceiling. The dining room is big enough for sixty to sit down for an evening meal. It has been my 'Shangri-la'. The house and the family have given me so much throughout my life, I had to survive for their sake.

My other interests include being President of the South Petherton Combined Arts Society. I have been a member for more than 30 years. The Society promotes. 'art' in the form of painting. There are at present 30 members of the art section and also a group that performs modern and more conventional drama with more than 30 members.

There is also the choir of which I have already written. Recently we have enlarged our repertoire and performed more modern music by Andrew Lloyd Webber and Leonard Bernstein, among other modern composers.

I am a member of the Parochial Church Council of St Peter and St Paul, South Petherton, being especially keen that the financial aspects of church life are kept in a healthy state. I am a regular communicant at the Sunday Eucharist at 9.30 a.m. and attend with unfailing regularity as part of my therapy. I like going to the service to offer thanks that I have recovered so far. I receive inspiration to try harder during the following week. But, above all I can gauge what progress I have made in the past week. Am I standing better? Am I standing taller? Is my right shoulder more level with my left shoulder? Can I hold my prayer book, my hymn book better than last week? Can I sing with greater enjoyment? Am I able to see all the people clearly within the church? Can I read all the hymns in the hymn book. These seem to be very simple things to be done but I find it most interesting to see what progress I have made.

I am also Chairman of the Relief in Need charity in South Petherton. This is a small committee of senior citizens who are working as trustees. We meet twice a year and have power to distribute the funds, to deserving people and causes.

I am a member of the South Petherton Business' Association and have been asked by the committee to act as an adviser in the future. The village is a super place and I am privileged to be an active member within the community.

Since my father's death in 1967 I have been a member of the South Petherton Parish Council. I have tried to carry on the great family tradition of service to the community. Grampa Vaux was a member of the Parish Council when it was first formed. He remained a member until his untimely death in 1943. My father then became a member until his death. I find it most worthwhile. Society has to be led by people with experience and knowledge.

In the autumn of 1989, a public meeting was held to discuss the possibility of putting on a community play. Ninety per cent of the audience thought that a 'play' meant *Hamlet* or a *She Stoops to Conquer*. We were very wrong. A Community Play is a new, original work about and for the community. A well known national playwright, Bruce Bedford, was commissioned by the South Somerset District Council to write a play about South Somerset. As a result of this meeting, the inevitable committee was formed. As a long standing member of the community, I was asked to be a member of the steering committee and at its first meeting I was appointed Chairman. Because of my long family involvement with all aspects of village affairs, I was able to act as leader of the research group.

We had fifteen people, mostly over fifty, who were first class at delving into the past, each one searching a particular facet of the village's story.

What was the community like centuries ago?

What did they do when they went to work?

How many shops were in the village?

How many farms and farm workers in the district?

Characters and their part in Petherton's history.

There has been a wealth of information uncovered and it may be possible to write several plays about the district.

We had a sub-committee which was responsible for fund raising. Their target was £5,000 and £1,500 from a grand draw. When all the funds were in the bank, the total raised was £9,000.

Other members of the steering committee were involved in getting grants from various official bodies. Commercial sponsorship in this type of venture was very important but it was very hard work for the lady responsible.

Publicity was most important and we had an enthusiastic sub-committee working on this aspect of the venture at that time.

In the Spring of 1990, the village community was beginning to talk about the community play in all aspects. The Colway Theatre Trust always acted as our guide and in the spring of 1990, they said we would need a special venue. It must be a building capable of holding 120 actors and actresses; there would be an orchestra of 20; there could be up to 500 in the audience and it should be possible to perform the play over a two-week period. This was a very tall order. Where could such a building in the village be found?

Several sleepless nights later I thought we could use two large barns at Wigborough Farm. My cousin Robert and the Colway Theatre Trust discussed the project at some length and it was finally agreed that the barns would be suitable for the purpose. Robert and Joan, their family and their staff were wonderful throughout the early part of 1991. Two barns of over 7,500 square feet each were emptied of all farm equipment and the play could start its rehearsals from February 1st. They would then be in use until the end of March 1991. This was an arrangement which Robert found quite acceptable. During the autumn of 1990 and with a residential professional play co-ordinator, Kate Cross, already working full time, workshops for actors and actresses, electricians, scenery setters etc took place at regular intervals.

The publicity machine was geared up with over 10,000 handbills to be distributed through various agencies in Somerset, Devon and Dorset. Costumes had to be made and a group of local needlewomen worked long and hard at this task.

Auditions took place just before Christmas 1990 and in early 1991, every man woman and 25 children or more

128

were given their various parts. For ten weeks many people thought of only one thing: *Listenstone* – that was the play's title. This would be a great success, we felt sure. The full dress rehearsal was on Sunday afternoon, March 10th and performances started on March 11th.

This is not the obvious place to tell the full story of *Listenstone*. Suffice it to say it was a huge success as a means of bringing hundreds of people into contact with one another, in a unique way. Many people have said, as Bruce Bedford said at a meeting in November 1989, 'That's a community play'.

I retell many of these incidents to show that the community play was an integral part of my recovery. I had been cruelly struck down in July 1986. The community had been most shocked, but they had helped me recover so far. Through the medium of the community play, I tried to repay part of that concern.

In the spring of 1991 after the community play had finished, Peggy and I felt that we needed another holiday. Where should we go? We thought that the most likely place would have to be to France. Again, another question came up. Should I be able to drive in France? How long could we stay? Would I be able to drive onto the ferry at Poole? Would I find driving on the right-hand side too much of an ordeal? Would there be many language difficulties?

We thought over these problems for some days and discussed them with some good friends in the village. We discovered that other friends had a villa in the South of France which we could stay in for two or three weeks.

It was a great thrill for me to be driving with confidence in my own ability, in a foreign country and without any great difficulty. Every new venture now must have a purpose for me. My own confidence had been completely shattered at the time of the stroke. This was a giant leap back to some form of normality.

During the next three weeks, we drove over 2,000 miles, of which I drove 1,200. I had a slight car accident in Montpellier. In England, it would have been the other driver's fault. In France perhaps it was my fault. Both cars suffered superficial damage. Nobody was injured. Both cars were drivable. After our names and addresses had been exchanged for insurance purposes, we drove away and continued our holiday.

I mention this incident in some detail for it illustrates that after 5 years, I had recovered sufficiently to take this accident with equanimity. Twelve months earlier and it may have been a very different story.

Two weeks were spent touring through the beautiful countryside of the southern slopes of the Massif Central. The sights and smells of the hundreds of varieties of wild flowers, reawakened within me long-forgotten scenes of rural Somerset that I knew when I was a boy. This reawakening will surely bear fruit when I come to write another book. We returned to Cherbourg by a more westerly route and I felt another great hurdle had been overcome.

The summer of 1991 saw a new character at work. I couldn't work in any meaningful way but at least I could drive my car. Philip had members of staff who required transport to the fields where they were picking up potatoes. It may have been only a little job but at least I felt wanted. I was able to ferry them in the mornings as early sometimes as 7.45. In the afternoon I was able to fetch them from work at the end of the day. This was, at last something I could do and be of use in a sensible way.

The autumn of 1991 was filled with therapeutic activities. Early in September, I was asked to attend a play reading organised by the Combined Arts Society.

An enterprising person thought that there was enough talent available in the district to produce Dylan Thomas' famous radio play *Under Milk Wood*. I went to the first play reading and was asked to read the part of Captain Cat, a blind retired sea captain. I hesitatingly agreed at first without knowing what Captain Cat said or was supposed to have done.

I did not know that he is a central character in the play, a part played by Hugh Griffiths, the famous radio actor in the BBC's original production. I hadn't done any acting since before I was married. I was very nervous and slightly diffident. I found learning the lines very difficult, some of which was probably due to my age and some due to brain damage, caused by the stroke. But the producer and other members of the cast were most sympathetic and helpful. We rehearsed the play throughout September, October and November.

It was produced during the last week of November 1991. When the time came, the nervousness had disappeared. I was suitably costumed in sailor's hat, navy blue roll-necked sailor's pullover, sea boots and an earring. To give the effect of the blindness I had borrowed a pair of smoke-coloured glasses of the 1930s. The strong Somerset voice and the feeling I was able to put into the evocative lines were well received by the audience. At the end I felt very elated. At last, after five and a half years, I had presented myself in company with a cast of thirty-five, before an audience and I hadn't been tongue-tied, stage struck or, lost for words. The whole exercise had done my self confidence an immeasurable amount of good.

Under Milk Wood was a direct spin-off from the community play. In fact *Listenstone* was still being talked about throughout 1991. Early in 1991 one of the members of our steering committee approached me about a competition being organised by the Somerset Community Council. It is an organisation supported by the County Council, District Councils and other interested bodies within the county of Somerset. It promotes all aspects of village life. It holds a biennial competition entitled Village Ventures.

The committee thought that we should present *Listenstone* as a village venture. We quickly contacted the office in Taunton, reserved some tickets for two people to see *Listenstone* one night and sent an application form with a programme, a tape recording and video cassette and waited for three months. In July 1991, we were visited by two Somerset judges. They came and asked many questions. We were told soon afterwards that we had been shortlisted as one of six within the county.

At the end of September, we were again visited, this time by two national judges. The ladies had worn some of the original costumes from *Listenstone* and there were many photographs on display. The steering committee put on an excellent job of presenting the play to complete strangers. In November 1991 we went to a prize-giving ceremony at Ashcott Village Hall near Street, Somerset. We were awarded a silver cup to be held, for two years for the all-round excellence of *Listenstone*. The public at large had undoubtedly thought the whole enterprise a great success.

In the autumn of 1992, the Combined Arts Society put on another great production of the *Christmas Carol* by Charles Dickens. It was adapted by our professional director, Ged McKenna, who had produced *Under Milk Wood*. It was performed five times in December. I was chosen to play two small parts – one of which was non-speaking. I felt in doing a play by Dickens I was finally re-establishing myself in the community.

For the stroke sufferer, this re-building of confidence

takes a long time. The determination to over-come seemingly impossible tasks can and must be appreciated by society generally.

12

THE FUTURE

These events of 1991 when taken together, represented for me a great step forward in my rehabilitation. Gone was any feeling of inadequacy. The clouds of self-doubt had drifted away. I felt able to face the community at large as a normal person, not able to walk normally and with my right arm hanging by my side but able to make a significant contribution to the affairs that surrounded me.

I have been very lucky during these years of recovery. They have been full of joy and sorrow, laughter and tears. My ruby wedding was on December 28th 1991. Throughout those 40 years especially since July 13 1986, my wife Peggy has been a tower of strength. Steadfast in faith at all times, practical in all things, economical with our money. In fact, to use a phrase from Dylan Thomas's *Under Milk Wood* It can be said of her as a character said: 'She's a proper ruby'.

When looking back, I thank God I had physical strength to survive and inward strength to record my innermost feelings during this period. This could only be done very near the incident of the stroke and in consequence some of my efforts have been very halting. I had nevertheless used any ability to write, as a self-imposed therapy.

My first effort at writing was a short article for *Hope*,

the magazine of the Chest Heart and Stroke Association. It was factual and was always sincere. My brain could function normally but my body was very disabled. My mind was still thinking 'what could I do to help other people overcome a stroke, any loss of speech and the general disability?' I wanted to give something of myself to society. It is not for me to tell anybody how to avoid having a stroke. Was I smoking too many cigars? Did I have too much full-cream milk and cream for breakfast with my cereals? I always liked the frying pan for my egg, bacon, sausages and potatoes every day! And, the Cheddar cheese. Part of the staple diet for farmers. Were those incidents recorded in this book so stressful? Was the tension within my own business so bad? I don't know. Nobody knows or will ever know the complete story. It took place. But for sufferers and carers alike, one can survive and live to tell the tale.

You, dear reader, are part of the therapy. I started writing the first draft of this book in the autumn of 1987. I couldn't write properly even with my left hand. So I got a tape recorder. I wrote very untidy longhand and spoke into a recorder. Friends Ann and then Brenda, typed from the recorder.

I tell you this because I have put at least 200,000 words on tape which has been used as part of my own therapy. A speech therapist said to me not very long ago, that speech therapy can be called speech stimulation so this book for you, the reader, has been an essential part of my speech therapy.

What does the future hold? For me and for the thousands like me, there is faith. One hundred thousand people a year – one every four minutes of the day and night suffer from a stroke. Not all as intense and deep as mine. Some are more severe, some have fatal consequences. But we must have faith, faith that medical science can help people to prevent strokes.

We must learn to eat a fat reduced diet with less salt or salty foods.

We must give up smoking – 100% give it up!

And we must have our blood pressure and cholesterol count taken at regular intervals.

I am afraid I hadn't taken any notice of medical advice and now rue the day.

Then there is the stress factor. I thought at the time this was the over-riding factor. Having written three drafts about my early life, I am more than ever convinced the stresses, the worries, and the teasing had a profound effect upon my early life. It wasn't possible to express my deepest feelings at the time. Nobody knew about every incident mentioned. But having written about them and released my innermost feelings to the world, I feel a lot better.

My body has been like an oak tree struck down by lightning, for the last six and a half years. The head is clearer now. There is more control over my lips and cheek. My speech is virtually normal. My legs and trunk are more in tune with the rest of my body. The right shoulder is slowly improving, it's the right hand that's the most troublesome.

13

AFTERWORD

In early September 1992, my son Stephen who lives at Charlbury, Oxfordshire telephoned me to say he had read a most interesting article in the *Independent on Sunday*. This article described in some detail the work being conducted by a research team at Odstock Hospital near Salisbury. The team is lead by a Dr Swain and his technicians and physiotherapists. They are engaged on basic research of neurological disorders. It has been found that it is of great benefit to stroke sufferers.

It consists of helping patients with walking difficulties and hand movements. The gait improvement is designed to stop the swinging of hips and to walk more naturally. The hand movement is designed to increase the use of the right hand. A patient had stated in the article that he could now stir a cup of tea with his right hand; shake hands with his right hand; and use his right hand to support the newspaper when it was being read. These are very basic movements and I could see that it would be of great benefit to me. In consequence I wrote to Dr Swain immediately. He replied asking for a referral notice from my general practitioner together with other details as to when I had the stroke, how severe it was and further notes from my physiotherapist. He also wanted a general account of my present condition. These were all collected and sent off to him.

A visit was duly arranged for early December 1992. The basis of much of this work is that a video recording is taken of the patient and shows on film exactly what you are doing at any particular time. Not only is your gait recorded but the speed at which you cover a particular stretch of the corridor in the hospital. Dr Swain informed me that he was waiting for authority from the highest level within the NHS to be able to continue and expand his work. This fortunately came through in 1993 and I have now started a new course of treatment with him. I will endeavour to describe it in layman's terms, devoid of the technicalities which the physiotherapists and the doctors may provide.

I went to Odstock in early May 1993. I changed into a pair of shorts so that the camera could see exactly how my leg swung to one side when walking. The physiotherapist and the senior technician also stuck small yellow discs on the outside of the right and left leg starting at the toes going through the heels, the knee, the hip and a single yellow disc was placed on the coccyx at the bottom of the spine. These yellow pads were clearly visible on the V.D.U. screen when I saw them myself at the end of the filming.

The use of V.D.U.'s and video cameras enables the physiotherapists and the doctors to see accurately how the patient is progressing and allows the patients themselves to take part in any work which is being carried out. The film can be slowed down considerably and then put into reverse so that the patient and the doctor and the physiotherapist can examine in even greater detail exactly what is happening at any one time.

I also had to fill in a questionnaire which went into great detail and consisted of three foolscap pages. I was then wired and measured up with tapes around my middle and around my wrist which measured my heartbeat and pulse rate. Further exercises were done up and down stairs and when standing up and sitting down from a chair. When this was over the technicians fed all the information into a computer and eventually the treatment started.

The experiment is divided into two groups of people, one group will have electrical stimulation upon their leg and the other group will have normal advanced physiotherapy. Unluckily, I am in the second group and will be having advanced physiotherapy for 6 weeks or so. However it will be possible to have the electrical stimulation when this advanced physiotherapy is over. I look forward now to the end of July when this physiotherapy will finish.

Dr Swain and his team have been working not only on leg movements, also on arm and hand movements. The research is at a very early stage but I am quite sure that it will not be too long before they are able to give me some improvement. As I stated before, a return to dancing is my long-term aim. The target has been given to them and they feel that it may be possible to accomplish.

Jane Berridge, the Chief Physiotherapist working in Dr Swain's team, has given me an encouraging piece of news concerning the 'Dropped Foot Syndrome' which is the name given to the problems which I have with my gait.

In the first place, the electrical stimulation consists of a small pad placed under the heel of the left foot. A thin lead is then taken up through the left trouser leg and down through the right leg. Two pads are strategically placed on the outside of the right shin about three inches below the right knee. A small electrical battery is placed in the pad under the left heel. As I walk, my left heel presses down on the pad which activates the stimulator and makes my right foot lift up in the normal way. It is not possible to know how long this form of treatment will be necessary. Maybe forever, but, who's worrying? It will make walking easier with a natural gait. Walking will be less tiring, more enjoyable. Jane Berridge, also gave me most encouraging news for all stroke patients in the future.

Advanced medical technology is progressing rapidly. Within a few years the stimulator may be fitted under the skin of the affected leg in the same way that a heart patient is fitted with a pace maker. Perhaps that long term aim is closer to fruition than I thought.

May I now draw this story to a conclusion and place my innermost thoughts with you whether you are a carer for a patient, a stroke patient or just a general member of the public. This whole episode since 1986 has been a very difficult, troublesome, traumatic episode in a life filled as it has been, to capacity. May I say to stroke patients: 'never give up trying – it's a long hard and very stony road but the reward, at the end, is a life that is as close to normality as it's possible to be. One must never despair however difficult life is and from the ashes of 1986, perhaps a new phoenix will arise to give greater pleasure and receive enhanced benefits from life in the future.